QUINTESSENTIAL STYLE

CULTIVATE AND COMMUNICATE YOUR SIGNATURE LOOK

JANNA BEATTY
WITH SHARON WHITE

Quintessential Style: Cultivate and Communicate Your Signature Look

Published by Wheatmark®
1760 East River Road, Suite 145
Tucson, Arizona 85718 U.S.A.
www.wheatmark.com

Cover Design by Sarah Jo White

Illustrations by Jackie Barefield

ISBN: 978-1-62787-129-7
LCCN: 2014951952

To my wondrous clients:
Thank you for teaching me.
Thank you for being you.
—J.B.

To the brightest stars in my universe,
Joe, Becky, and Sarah Jo.
With love and gratitude.
—S.W.

Drum with Intention
and Joy!
Jenna

quin·tes·sen·tial

kwintəˈsenCHəl/

adjective

1. the pure and essential essence of something or someone

2. of or pertaining to the most perfect embodiment

TABLE OF CONTENTS

INTRODUCTION ix

∿ 1 ∿
Personal PACKAGING 1

∿ 2 ∿
Who Are You . . . TODAY? 7

∿ 3 ∿
Humans Look BETTER IN COLOR! 17

∿ 4 ∿
Line & Design . . . THE ART OF ILLUSION 33

∽ 5 ∾
Wardrobe ABCs...47

∽ 6 ∾
Your Closet Is A RIVER 63

∽ 7 ∾
Shopping: CREATING YOUR PERSONAL COLLECTION...........75

∽ 8 ∾
Let's Face It . . . IT'S ALL ABOUT THE SKINCARE............................85

∽ 9 ∾
Makeup DESIGN 97

∽ 10 ∾
Personal & Professional POLISH 119

FINAL THOUGHTS 129

ACKNOWLEDGMENTS 133

REFERENCES 135

ABOUT THE AUTHORS 137

INTRODUCTION

"Each of us has treasures.
The hunt can be fun."

—*Janna Beatty*

"*You look amazing!*" is usually what I am thinking as I gaze across a crowd gathered when I show up to give a presentation. Interestingly enough, I am there to coach my audience on the power of visual appearance and give them tips for achieving *their* objectives, but they arrive already looking impeccable simply because I am their guest.

And when people find out I am a professional image consultant, they frequently comment, "I bet you just wish you could walk up to perfect strangers and tell them how to fix themselves up." This has always baffled me. As a matter of fact, I have thought that so rarely over the past three decades, you probably wouldn't believe me if I told you.

I consider myself to be merely an observant bystander. My job is to share knowledge with my clients and teach them to "see" themselves more clearly. While the media is busy telling us how we are "supposed to look," my focus is on unveiling the diversity of each individual. After all, the depth of our beauty lies in our diversity.

Recently I came across an article that featured tips from outstanding businesswomen based on the mistakes and successes that had affected their careers. The number one tip: *"Don't fix it, find it!"*

Truer words could not have been issued, especially where my clients are concerned. A commonly held myth for many people is that they would be happier, more successful, more fulfilled if only they could *fix* themselves. What they don't realize is that they aren't broken—they came into this world exactly as they were meant to. The beauty is already there. They simply need to *find* it.

You were delivered into this world with your own genetic blueprint, physical traits, personality, and all the characteristics that make you *quintessentially* you. Oh, what a glorious being you are!

I believe signature style comes not by mimicking some iconic image, not by fitting into some specific size, not by wearing what is currently *en vogue*. Personal style is just that—personal. What you have to be is yourself. It's not about styling an outfit; it's about styling *who you are.*

The intention of this book is to help you become your own image consultant. I want to share concepts I have learned from my clients, over the past 30 years, which will hopefully enlighten the way you view yourself and the way you communicate who you are to the world.

Welcome to *your* self-discovery. The adventure awaits.

"The privilege of a lifetime is being who you are."

–Joseph Campbell

～ 1 ～

Personal
PACKAGING

*"Clothes make the man.
Naked people have little or no influence on society."*

–Mark Twain

In his groundbreaking book, *Dress for Success,* John T. Molloy asserts that it is impossible to dress in a neutral way. Every garment has a socioeconomic rating. Studies show that up to 95 percent of the messages we convey are nonverbal. That means people are more likely to believe information cues based on how we look, rather than what we say.

Think about it. Without conscious consideration, you can immediately spot elements of a provocatively dressed woman (tight, short, low cut). Just as noticeable are the hallmarks of a powerful, confident business executive (pressed, tailored, professional). Different outfits have the power to evoke different responses from the observer.

Oftentimes when I go into companies to do training, I show comparative photos of professionals. Then I ask attendees to guess which person they think might be a manager, which person makes more money, which is more highly educated, which has a better social life, etc. Based exclusively on these photographs, participants make judgments about occupation, income, education, and possibly even morals, within seconds. These responses prove that although we have been taught "you can't judge a book by its cover," we usually do.

Impression Criteria

Public speakers recognize that their audiences sum them up within 60 seconds. The cliché "you never get a second chance to make a first impression" is verified by studies that have shown it actually takes 14 exposures to "undo" a wrong first impression. What is really taking place during this initial introduction is termed *impression criteria.*

The moment you see a person, you instinctively assess his/her race, gender, and age. If you have ever listened to a radio description of a police suspect, these are the first three identifying

IMPRESSION CRITERIA		
FIXED:	**Skin Color**	
	Gender	
	Age	
FLEXIBLE:	**Appearance**	
	Clothing	
	Hair	
	Makeup	
	Facial Expression	
	Movement	
	Voice	
	Personal Space	
	Touch	

attributes. (For example, white, male, late 30s.) These three elements of appearance are fixed.

But some impression criteria are flexible, that is, they can be altered in varying degrees. They are (in descending order of impression impact): appearance, facial expression, movement, voice, personal space, and touch.

Appearance can be broken down into three categories: clothing, hair, and makeup. Eyewear should also be considered, since glasses can completely change your look. But because about 90 percent of our bodies are covered with clothing, it's easy to understand why *what we wear* makes a powerful statement to the world about *who we are.*

As a professional image and color consultant, my job is to help my clients get more of anything they want in life by working with their appearance. And now that you recognize a significant portion of your image is conveyed nonverbally, recognize also that you have the ability to be perceived differently if you dress differently. In essence, you can giftwrap yourself any way you choose.

Begin asking yourself what it is you want to communicate through your visual appearance. I'm here to help you do it. Now let's get started!

The image consulting industry was born out of America's marketing savvy, which first turned toward the individual creation of the Hollywood movie star.

"Three-tenths of a good appearance is due to nature; seven-tenths to dress."

—Chinese saying

CLIENT FEEDBACK
MY GREATEST REWARD

Without question, the most gratifying moments in my professional career have been those times when I've gotten feedback from clients who have literally transformed their lives simply by gaining new insights about themselves. Recently, I received this note from a client:

Dear Janna,

Before I met you, I had no idea that I could communicate who I was through my appearance. But it didn't really matter, because I couldn't figure out how to fully put a look together anyway.

It was during my consultations with you that I realized my physical self-perception was far from accurate. I made negative judgments about myself based on what I thought I saw. But once I began to see my body objectively and learned how to dress in the most flattering ways for me (not for someone else), the self-doubt and the confusion vanished.

I no longer have mixed messages about how I should look. Now I realize what I want to communicate, and I show up for every occasion feeling good about my appearance.

Knowing how to visually present the most flattering and authentic version of myself to the world is true empowerment. The consequence is becoming emotionally free to simply "be present" in my own life.

We may try to deny it, but how we think and feel about ourselves is directly related to how we visually present ourselves, and vice versa. If we change our approach to either of these ideas, it will profoundly affect the other. That was a mighty revelation for me.

I now have the confidence to "own" my look instead of allowing other people to dictate it for me. I don't know how to satisfy them, but I know exactly how to satisfy myself. I've taken charge of my life. I know who I am, and I'm not afraid of it. I'm prepared and ready for the task. I have something to contribute.

How freeing it is to give yourself permission to be "who you are."

∾ 2 ∾

Who Are You . . . TODAY?

"Be yourself . . . everyone else is already taken."

—Oscar Wilde

Can you remember back to a time when you felt absolutely amazing in an outfit? Maybe it was a prom dress or an interview suit. Perhaps it was your wedding gown or new back-to-school clothes. Do you recall that joy, and any specifics about how that outfit made you feel?

When I visit a client's closet, one of the first things I ask them to do is, "Show me a garment that looks *like you*." There are usually racks of clothing and accessories, but you would be surprised how long it takes them to actually choose an outfit that categorically and undeniably communicates who they are.

Your appearance should be an outlet for your individuality, a canvas for creativity. Clothes speak volumes about your personality. So I ask you, "What outfit do you own right now that expresses your personality and cries out, *This is ME!*"

Years ago, a lovely group of ladies visited my studio. We were discussing personal essence as it relates to signature style. One dear woman seemed hesitant to join the conversation. Finally, looking quite perplexed, she asked, "What if you *don't know* your style?" I immediately pulled out three clothing catalogs and handed them to her. I posed this question: "If you had to order *all* your outfits from just one of these catalogs, which one would you choose?" Oddly enough, every other person in the room seemed to know exactly which catalog she would pick, but until she was forced to examine them herself, she was totally confounded when it came to her own style. She chose the catalog we all knew she would, since the clothing matched her personality to a tee—elegant, understated, and classic.

"Know Thyself."

Back in 400 B.C., Socrates may have very well acted as the first image consultant, imploring his listeners to *get to know themselves*. Have you thought about it lately? Who are you . . . TODAY? I emphatically stress the word *today*, because I don't mean who you were five or ten years ago, I absolutely mean who you are at this very moment.

I would estimate about 80 percent of my clients come to me for advice during some type of transitional period in their lives. Some may be entering back into the workforce, some have just gone through a divorce, some have become empty nesters, some have recently lost a significant person in their life. They are not the same people they were 20 or even 10 years ago. In fact, many are struggling to find their identity and/or reinvent themselves. My job is to teach them how to engineer their appearance to achieve specified results.

Perhaps you have not thought about your style for a while. Maybe never. The following questions are meant to prompt you to ask yourself *who you are today,* and inspire you to think about *where you want to go* in order to accomplish those things that are most meaningful to you.

PERSONAL STYLE INVENTORY

Take a look at the words below and rank them on a scale of 1 (low) to 10 (high), based on how they relate to your **personal style now.**

_____	Sporty	_____	Casual
_____	Friendly/approachable	_____	Energetic
_____	Classic	_____	Natural
_____	Professional/business-like	_____	Trendy
_____	Authoritative	_____	Credible
_____	Elegant	_____	Refined
_____	Distinguished	_____	Poised
_____	Quality	_____	Powerful
_____	Gracious	_____	Alluring
_____	Sensuous	_____	Flirtatious
_____	Sexy	_____	Quirky/whimsical
_____	Creative	_____	Exotic
_____	Original	_____	Artistic
_____	Dramatic	_____	Sophisticated
_____	Fashionable	_____	Bold
_____	Other (_____)	_____	Other (_____)

After ranking, order them the way you would ultimately like them to be.

Now, write down three words, any words, to describe how **you would like to be perceived when people look at you.**

1. _____ 2. _____ 3. _____

These words may vary depending upon the occasion, e.g., formal you, social you, business you, leisure you, etc.

If you had to order your clothing from only one catalog, or shop in only one clothing store, which one would you choose?

_____

What do you think is the most attractive part of your body? (If nothing comes to mind, think about what feature/asset you are most often complimented on.)

_____

What are your favorite colors to wear?

_____

What is your absolute favorite accessory to wear? (Excluding your wedding ring.) Why?

_____

Do you think you are currently dressing in a way that reveals the unique essence of your personality? _____

If not, what is your biggest style obstacle(s) right now?

_____

What would you like to communicate about your personality to the world through your clothing choices?

_____

When it comes to your personal style, how would you like to be remembered?

_____

_____

Self-Sabotage

In our high-tech world, visual and virtual images of beauty bombard us at every turn. How do you internalize those images? Do media and technology help you feel better or worse about yourself?

*"We get information 24/7,
and it's faster than the heart can digest."*

—Mark Nepo

The following questions may help determine whether you are subconsciously sabotaging your self-confidence:

- Do you wait for others to dictate your style, instead of trusting your own instincts?
- Do you see beauty, style, and confidence in others, but doubt it in yourself?
- Do you compare yourself to others, perhaps even celebrities?
- Is it possible you are dressing to impress others?
- Are you consistently critical of yourself?
- Do you accept others the way they are?
- Are you holding onto past insults or remarks that have caused you to feel negative about yourself?

It is important to remember that when it comes down to it, you have control over your feelings and responses to all of the above. It's *your choice.*

Intentional Dressing

Defining the way you ultimately want to be perceived and following that lead by dressing accordingly is called *intentional dressing.* It sounds complicated, but it's not. Intentional dressing simply means taking time to think about *why* you are getting dressed, and *what* you are getting dressed for. Answering these two questions can help you dress for any situation.

Have you ever returned home from an event and said to yourself, "I wish I'd worn something else." Well, we all have, but most likely it's because you didn't take time to dress with intention.

In my business, I get asked to dress clients for special occasions quite often. And the first

Years ago, I made an appearance at a local bookstore. The subject of my presentation focused on choosing the most flattering necklines for different face shapes. I selected a woman from the audience to be my model. She had the most perfectly round face I had ever seen.

When she came up, she looked at me and proclaimed, "I know why you picked me. Because I have the pointiest chin in the room." The audience erupted with laughter. And I had to take another look at her to make sure I hadn't missed something. For some reason, unbeknownst to me, she was under the impression she had the spikiest chin in the land, instead of the full-moon face I was beholding.

Later that evening, during a conversation with her, I discovered that as a child, the woman's sister had declared that her chin was so pointy, she looked like a witch. Decades had passed and this lovely woman was still holding onto that unfortunate childhood misconception.

question I will invariably ask my client is, "How would you like to be perceived when you enter the room?" The answers I've received have varied over the years. There are many motivations for dressing. Some want to look feminine and romantic, or authoritative and powerful, while others simply ask to look taller and thinner.

How many times have I dressed a first wife (perhaps for her child's wedding), who knows full well that the new, younger, second wife will be in attendance? My client's intention is almost always to look better than the new wife. (I didn't say younger, I said better.)

Your Personal Comfort Zone

Another important element to consider when dressing is your *comfort zone,* and your personality has everything to do with your comfort zone. If you are an outgoing, gregarious person, you may want all eyes focused on you, so over-the-top, flamboyant apparel may be your preference, and lies perfectly within your range of comfort. However, if you are more introverted and reserved, this type of dressing probably isn't for you. But that's not to say you can't dress to be noticed.

Style is all about communicating who you are through the language of clothing. And dressing is all about making choices that support your intentions. I believe self-knowledge is the key to self-empowerment. The more comfortable you become in your own skin (warts and all), the more confidence you gain in choosing clothing that matches your true essence. And ultimately, it becomes easier and easier to dress with signature style.

STYLE AND YOUR PERSONALITY

Just as there are many aspects to you and your personality, every outfit projects a style personality of its own. Do your clothes reflect what you want to represent to the world?

Think about which kind of clothing could make you feel:

Feisty	Athletic
Cute	Sophisticated
Sensual	Peaceful
Put together	Noticeable
Mysterious	Invisible
Radiant	Romantic

"Find out who you are—on purpose."

–Dolly Parton

CREATE YOUR OWN
"PERSONAL STYLE STATEMENT"

Have you ever wondered why you don't feel completely confident with your clothing choices? Or why an outfit may look absolutely stunning on someone else, but awful on you? The answer could be that you are not making style decisions that support "your authentic self."

You probably already have a personal style statement lodged somewhere in your subconscious. Let's try to define it more precisely.

Begin by jotting down a few words that describe how you would like to be perceived in your life and in your style. What is it you truly want to communicate with your appearance? (Refer to "Personal Style Inventory" for a list of adjectives.) These terms should accurately reflect your true spirit and the essence of how you would like to be represented.

_____

_____

Now turn those words into a phrase that summarizes your personal style:

_____

_____

This is your Personal Style Statement.

Simply by referring to this brief and well-chosen phrase, it is possible to gain more direction and greater assurance with decision-making, not only when dealing with clothing and appearance but in every facet of your life.

Here are some examples of Personal Style Statements:

- Rebellious and stand-alone, not afraid of making an impact
- Invitingly chic with casual flair
- Friendly, witty, and ready for fun
- Understated elegance that whispers wealth

You should feel free to write anything knowing you have the option of never sharing your statement with another living soul. And you can rewrite your statement anytime you like.

THE ETERNALLY VEXING QUESTION:
WHAT SHALL I WEAR?

Do you ever have indecision about what to wear to an upcoming event? When you receive an invitation, there are five important criteria to consider when choosing an outfit.

Time?　　Daytime /After 5 p.m./ After 8 p.m.
　　　　　　The later in the day, the more formal the occasion.

Event?　　Ball game/picnic/cocktail party/wedding

Location?　Home/office/country club/church

People?　　Family/friends/professional acquaintances/strangers

Objective?　What is your purpose at this event? How do you want to be perceived?

∽ 3 ∽

Humans Look
BETTER IN
COLOR!

*"Color is the first thing seen,
and the last thing remembered."*

–*Janna Beatty*

I love color! Knowledge of color, and how color showcases each individual, is the foundation for my entire profession as an image consultant.

Color experts Joanne Nicholson and Judy Lewis-Crum insist, "Color is the quintessential element in dressing successfully . . . But it's also probably the most overlooked."

So what's the problem? Don't women recognize which colors look best on them? Well, in my business, I find that a very small percentage of people consistently wear their most flattering colors.

There have been many theories about color since ancient times. Because color is light, the complexities and applications of color are infinite and changing. To package color into a tidy system is like harnessing a rainbow.

Current-day consumers have been exposed to differing and conflicting color theories. The most popular is the cool/warm theory, which, in my personal opinion, has oversimplified and greatly limited the image consulting industry.

Well-meaning mothers and friends, whose ideas come through the tint of their own lenses, have also shared their notions about color. Combine this with individual color preferences and psychological research substantiating the theory that it is impossible to view ourselves objectively, and we begin to feel overwhelmed at the thought of ever finding our most flattering hues.

In truth, *anyone* can wear *any* color in the spectrum, warm or cool, provided it is **the correct shade and the correct clarity.** Of course you can wear any colors you wish, but if you want to look your absolute best, doesn't it makes sense to learn which hues harmonize with and enhance your natural coloring?

Have you ever wondered why some people can get away with wearing bold, bright outfits and others can't? Or why someone wearing pastels looks absolutely terrific, but others who put on the same gentle colors appear totally washed out? The answer is that certain colors complement you naturally while others can overpower or detract from your personal coloring.

Refer to our website www.qstylethebook.com for more complete color information.

Choosing the most flattering garments involves not only decisions about which colors to wear but, more specifically, selecting the correct shades that complement you. And, believe it or not, choosing the right patterns, prints, and textures of fabrics is also an important element that comes into play.

LEARNING TO "SEE" CLEARLY

Sometimes simply learning to identify colors that look *too dull* on you and colors that look *too bright* on you is the best way to begin understanding the concept of clarity.

While weeding out garments in my husband's closet, I came across a throng of ties that had amassed over the years. Some of the ties had been gifts, some he had bought for himself, some were hand-me-downs. I pulled out a lot of ties that he admitted he no longer wore, so they were free to be donated. There were also some that weren't particularly the most flattering colors for him, so they were discarded. But there was one particular maroon tie that he claimed as one of his favorites. He didn't want to part with it, because it was the only red tie he owned and he usually wore it once or twice a week.

I told him I wouldn't throw out the maroon tie if he would consider wearing it only twice a month instead of twice a week. On all the other days, he would wear any of the ties left hanging in his closet. He agreed.

My plan was for him to "see" himself—not just wearing colors, but wearing his most flattering colors. Then when he put on the maroon tie (which I knew was much too dull a shade of red for him), he would immediately notice a difference. That is exactly what happened. Within the first month of the experiment, he was ready to rid himself of the drab maroon tie and opt for others that made him look brighter and more energized.

Once you understand the importance of clarity in colors and discover that every shade is different—some clearer and brighter, some more muted and grayed—hopefully you will begin to "see" which colors work best with *you*.

Clarity is the element in color that describes how bright, dull, or toned down it is. If you were to mix brown or gray pigment into a bright color, it would not be as bright. And if you have ever purchased a can of paint and found it to be too bright, you probably returned it to the paint store where they simply added a burnt umber to neutralize or calm the pigment.

Determining clarity is foundational for deciding which colors harmonize with each other and, more importantly, with the individual. If you wear colors with too little clarity (dull), they can dim you down, while colors with too much clarity (too bright) may overpower you.

How can you test clothing to see if it is the correct clarity? Place the garment at your face, and ask yourself: "Does this color complement my skin and eyes, or is it dull and drab?"

Pattern Size is also an important element that can determine whether a garment either flatters or detracts. Have you ever seen a woman wearing clothing that made her fade into the background, or appear weak or frumpy? Or a woman wearing an outfit with a pattern that so completely overwhelmed her, it looked as if the outfit was wearing her? If so, she made a poor pattern choice.

We have been taught that if you are petite, you should wear small prints, and if you are larger/taller, your best choices are bigger/bolder prints. Not necessarily. Your color type is a better gauge as to what size pattern you should be wearing than your stature. (Refer to Color Type Charts for more information.)

My older sister was a petite 4'9" and weighed about 85 pounds as a senior in high school. I was a foot taller and weighed more. When we shopped together, clerks brought her the tiny prints and me the larger ones. But, based on our color types (she being a Contrast, I being a Muted), she was actually the one who could wear larger, bolder prints, while medium prints looked best on me.

COLOR 1 ASSOCIATES

The color system I prefer is the "Color 1 Associates" method developed by Joanne Nicholson and Judy Lewis-Crum. Here are some Color 1 guidelines to help you determine your individual color type.

Your Skin Color

Before you can establish which colors are most flattering for you, it is vital that you take a good look at your skin. Without makeup, in natural light, try to determine the **color of your skin,** e.g., ivory, pink, beige, olive, golden, brown, dark brown, red brown, golden brown, or other.

What is your skin color? _____

Your Hair Color

Next, take a look at your hair and determine your *main* **hair color and highlights.** Are you platinum blonde, golden blonde, ash blonde, light brown, dark brown, red, black, silver, white, or other?

What is your main hair color? _____

Your Contrast Level

Now you can determine the contrast level between your hair and your skin. **Contrast** is the level of difference between the lightest element and the darkest element of the whole. (Elizabeth Taylor would be high contrast with her dark hair and light skin, while Grace Kelly would be low contrast with light hair and light skin.)

Do you have a high contrast or low contrast level? _____

This information applies to women of all ethnicities. Every skin color has an undertone or highlight. It may be pink, beige, olive, golden, red, etc. Look at the inside of your forearm for the best indication of your skin's specific color. It may be difficult to detect undertones and highlights yourself. Consult a color professional if you need help.

Look on the following pages for descriptions of the four main Color 1 color types: Gentle, Muted, Contrast, and Light-Bright. Once you have determined your particular color type, you can find suggestions for colors, prints, patterns, and fabrics that are most flattering to you.

(It is possible to be a Combination Color Type, which means you fit into one of the four basic types, but can wear colors recommended in a different group. Some color types are easily recognizable. Others may not be so cut and dry. Don't become discouraged as you search out your best colors.)

❧ GENTLE ❧

Skin: Ivory or pink beige

Hair: Blonde, light to dark brown with ash, golden, or strawberry highlights

Best Prints:

- Small and medium scale
- The larger the print, the more blended-looking it needs to be
- Plaids, stripes, checks, and dots should be very blended and have medium contrast
- Can wear florals and watercolor prints
- Small amounts of pure white

Fabric Weight: Light/medium weights

Fabric Texture: Smooth textures

Avoid:

- High contrast
- Black, navy, or dark brown with pure white
- Large prints
- Rough textures

Great Colors: Pinks and pastels

Remember: Monochromatic looks

Clarity: Soft, toned-down colors

GENTLE

∽ MUTED ∽

Skin: Ivory, beige, pink-brown beige, olive, or golden-brown beige

Hair: Red or light to medium-dark brown hair with red, bronze, rust, or caramel highlights

Best Prints:

- Small and medium scale designs are best
- Muted color types over 5'6" may wear very blended-looking large patterns
- Plaids, stripes, checks, and florals are fine if they are blended or have medium contrast
- Dots may also be worn as long as they do not have strong contrast
- Leafy patterns, triangle shapes

Fabric Weight: Any weight

Fabric Texture: Maximum texture

Avoid:

- Pure white with black or navy
- High contrast
- Tiny patterns/prints

Great Colors: Orange, purple, green, teal

Remember: Texture

Clarity: Slightly toned-down colors

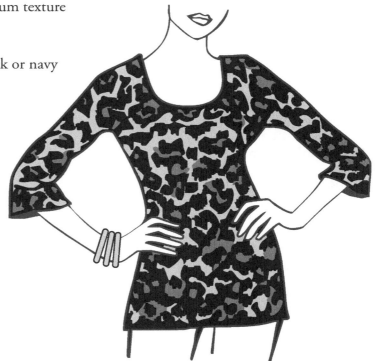

MUTED

∽ CONTRAST ∽

Skin: Ivory or olive skin

Hair: Dark brown to black hair

Best Prints:

- Medium to bold scale prints
- Plaids, stripes, dots, checks, and florals should have distinct strong contrast and definite design
- Dramatic, high-impact combinations
- Black and white is a signature look
- Shiny fabrics are great

Fabric Weight: Any weight

Fabric Texture: All textures

Avoid:

- Blended-looking prints
- Light-weight looking prints
- Dull colors
- Tiny/small patterns

Great Colors: Red, royal blue, bright green, bumblebee yellow

Remember: Can wear pure white

Clarity: Bold, bright, clear colors

CONTRAST

∾ LIGHT-BRIGHT ∾

Skin: Golden or ivory skin

Hair: Blonde, caramel, or medium-brown hair with golden highlights

Best Prints:

- Small and medium scale designs are best
- Plaids, stripes, dots, checks, and florals are fine if they have high contrast and small pattern
- Fabrics must have light background and look very lightweight

Fabric Weight: Light/medium weight

Fabric Texture: Light/medium looking texture

Avoid:

- Toned-down colors
- Dull colors
- Rough textures
- Saturated colors

Great Colors: Red/white/blue, turquoise, coral

Remember: Fabrics with light backgrounds

Clarity: Clear, light, bright colors

LIGHT-BRIGHT

COLOR TYPE COMPARISONS

GENTLE

MUTED

CONTRAST

LIGHT-BRIGHT

COLOR TYPES

" . . . color is so powerful that it can produce
unconscious physical and emotional reactions.
It can excite, calm, draw you towards,
or move you away from it."

–Sybil Henry

A Word about Neutrals

Neutral colors such as black, brown, gray, navy, beige, ivory, and white do not belong to any specific color group. It is advantageous to learn which neutrals look best on you. Not everyone looks spectacular in black. One may find navy more complementary in showcasing eyes, hair, and skin tone. White is often tricky to wear. If the whites of your eyes and your teeth are very white, you can probably safely wear pure white at your face. If not, off-white or ivory may be a better choice.

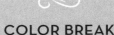

COLOR BREAK

Don't rush to throw out every black, white, or non-flattering neutral you own, thinking it may not be your best shade. Create a "color break" between your face and a less than flattering clothing color simply by using accessories. A complementary scarf, pashmina, sweater, or colorful jewelry worn at your neck will instantly brighten your face. Lipstick works, too. The more flattering accessory next to your face will negate the less flattering neutral.

Practical Matters

The purpose of the Color 1 system is to enable anyone to develop his/her own color sense, so they can quickly determine which colors are the most flattering. Think how this knowledge could simplify your life by eliminating poor color choices in clothing, makeup, hair color, and accessories. Think of all the time and money you can save, not to mention the mistakes and frustration you can avoid.

Over the years, the greatest reward clients have reported from having their colors charted is their increased self-confidence. Personal style teamed with flattering colors always works in creating outfits that express your true essence and ultimately make you feel fabulous.

Of course humans cannot be clumped into categories. Our uniqueness is the definitive determinant of our beauty. Color analysis is a supremely intricate and complicated beast. If you want to be absolutely sure of your color type, you may want to meet with a certified color analyst.

More Tips on Color

- As we mature, coloring fades in our face and in our lips, so it is important to replenish color with a flattering shade of lipstick or blush. If you don't wear lipstick, a pair of complementary colored earrings or necklace will do the job.

- When you try on a new shade of lipstick, don't focus simply on your lips— look at your skin and your eyes. A truly complementary color will brighten and transform your entire face.

- When you are in the dressing room, don't look into the mirror until you have put your entire outfit on. Then turn, look at yourself and ask: "Does this color make me look fabulous? Is it too bright? Does it wash me out? Is the print too large or too small?" If you see yourself, and BAM—YOU LOOK AWESOME, your color choice is the right one.

- When you look in the mirror do you see you or your clothing? Have you become a headless horseman? If so, you may be wearing an outfit that is too bright or has too much contrast.

- The two best shoe colors: (1) a pair that matches your hair color, and (2) a skin-tone shade that blends completely with the color of your legs.

- Don't be afraid to mix it up! If one color looks complementary on you and another color looks complementary on you, try putting both colors on together for maximum mix-ability.

OVERRULING THE EMINENCE OF THE LBD

Karl Lagerfeld once said, "One is never over-dressed or underdressed with a little black dress." And who is about to argue with this cool German guy? But Coco Chanel might have had a much better notion when she wowed the world with this sweeping statement: "The best colour in the whole world is the one that looks good on you."

So herein lies the question—What if black does nothing for your skin, hair, and eyes? But navy, chocolate, or turquoise lights you up like a firecracker? Hmmm . . . Karl, what do you say? Wear the black, or wear the exquisite color that transforms you?

It's not that black can't be fabulous. Just don't wear it if it's not fabulous on you.

Your new mantra: *I'm not styling an outfit—I'm styling me.*

Regardless of what anyone purports, professional or otherwise, the bottom line where color choice is concerned is: *HOW DO YOU FEEL* when you look in the mirror?

QUIZ TIME:

Okay, I know all of you have the ubiquitous LBD (maybe even three or four) hanging in your closet. What is the best way to make the black work for you when it isn't working for you?

ANSWER:

Add a color break. It may be a necklace, earrings, or pashmina in a complementary color, at your face. Voilá . . . instant verve. Oh, and don't forget the lipstick.

SENDING MESSAGES
WITH COLOR

Did you realize wearing certain colors sends unconscious messages? It's true. Colors have a myriad of meanings whether in professional settings, in marketing, psychologically, geographically, or even as far as cuisine is concerned.

The next time you send a photo, SnapChat, or decide to meet a new friend online, consider the signal you're sending with color. It could make or break a first impression.

BLUE—The majority of people say blue is their favorite color. It is perceived as social, friendly, approachable, and trustworthy.

RED—Red is the second most popular color. It is an adrenal stimulant and is often used to symbolize passion, sexiness, danger, and rebellion.

PINK—Pink relays a message of femininity, romance, and caring.

BLACK—Black is associated with sophistication and drama, and can also be perceived as mysterious, aloof, and menacing.

WHITE—White symbolizes purity, innocence, and openness.

YELLOW—Yellow is the most luminous color, so wear it when you want to be seen or if you want to stand out in a crowd. If you own an outfit that is simply too dull for your coloring, tossing on a yellow accent is a quick fix. It is sunny, optimistic, and fun . . . but that may not be for everyone.

GREEN—Green is earthy and natural, and a deep bluish-green can signify wealth.

PURPLE—Purple is highly symbolic. It can look royal and elegant, or light, fresh, and young.

ORANGE—Orange is energetic, exuberant, and warm, but may be perceived as less sophisticated, and perhaps not as luxurious-looking, by those in higher social classes.

After considering this information, ask yourself what message you want to convey. Color may help determine your answer. Do you want to be the life of the party, or simply blend in? The choice is yours.

～ 4 ～

Line & Design . . . THE ART OF ILLUSION

"The question is not what you look at, but what you see."

—Henry David Thoreau

Did you know that simply being aware of your body's shape can give you an edge to being well dressed? That's right. If you can identify your body type, then define how you would ultimately like to look, it is possible to *visibly* alter your shape. Once you know the basic principles of line and design you can make clothing work for you, no matter what your size. The secret is learning which lines do what.

Model Proportions

In Classic Greek and Roman art, the perfect proportion of the head to the rest of the body was considered 1:5. In modern times, that ratio has changed to about 1:7. However, in current fashion magazines, I have seen models with head to body ratios as high as 1:11. And although the latter proportions are actually quite "out of proportion," it is precisely these models that many women emulate.

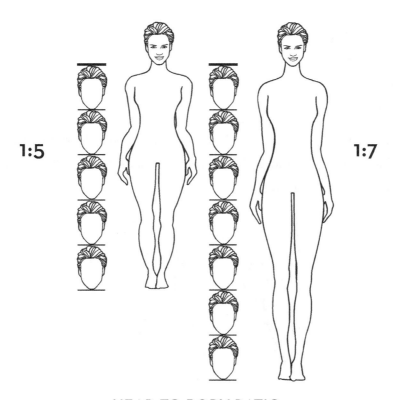

1:5   1:7

HEAD TO BODY RATIO

Fashion professionals with these proportions comprise less than one percent of the world's population. Since a fashion model's primary job is to showcase designers' collections, they are, in essence, acting as "human clothes hangers" on the runway.

Why mention any of this? Because so many of the clients I see are unhappy with their bodies. They often compare themselves to airbrushed beauties in magazines or to celebrities who retain full-time stylists (and trainers). These idealized women aren't really flawless. They just have help camouflaging the negative and enhancing the positive.

Once you understand your own body type you can do exactly what models and celebrities do—disguise the imperfections and accentuate the fabulous.

Learning Your Body Shape

Do you know your body shape? Did you notice I asked about *shape, not size?* Size may fluctuate through the years, but your body structure usually doesn't. There are five basic body shapes. I like to use letters of the alphabet to represent each.

- H–straight, rectangle
- O–round, apple
- A–teardrop, pear
- X–shapely, hourglass
- V–inverted triangle

Body shape is mainly determined by how balanced the shoulders and hips are. Ideally your shoulders should appear to be as wide, or slightly wider than, your hips. The illustration reveals shoulder/hip ratio.

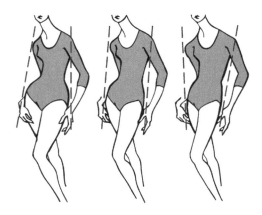

SHOULDER TO HIP RATIO

Very few of us have perfectly balanced bodies, but never discount your attributes. I have seen hourglass figures with great waists, and I have also seen pears with beautiful curves, apples with amazing legs, inverted triangles with strong shoulders, and rectangles that can wear practically anything. We all have something to flaunt.

And regardless of how heavy people are, even if they are obese, they still have a shape. Many people dismiss this idea and simply classify themselves as *large.*

"It's not the size you wear. It's how you wear your size."

–Adele Dallas Orr

Is it possible that once upon a time your body resembled an hourglass (X) and through the years it has transformed into more of a circle (O)? The important thing to do is to identify your body shape *now,* and embrace it. If you plan to lose weight, fine. If not, self-acceptance is the way to go.

The good news is that every one of us can customize our outfits to enhance

During all my years in this profession, the most comprehensive guide for disguising figure imperfections I have found is an amazing book titled *Flatter Your Figure.* Author Jan Larkey identifies every conceivable body type and explains ways to camouflage or enhance any area of a woman's figure. I highly recommend this book to all my clients.

our shapes. It's simply a matter of moving the lines in our clothing to attain a visual illusion of balance and proportion.

Your Vertical Body Type

Identifying your body's shape is relatively easy, but many women have never stopped to consider their vertical body type, which is determined by measurements taken from head to toe.

Your body is visually separated into two parts. The lower portion consists of your legs. The portion above your legs is called your torso and includes your head. There are two parts to your torso (upper and lower). The dividing line is your waist.

As you will discover, we are not all divided equally. And unfortunately, diet and exercise cannot alter your vertical body type (VBT). But once you have identified your VBT, you can make clothing choices that enhance and bring visual balance to your particular proportions.

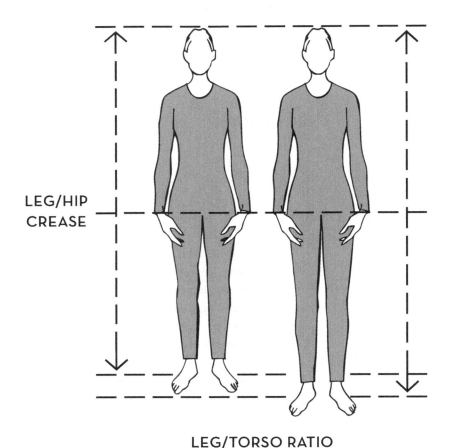

LEG/HIP CREASE

LEG/TORSO RATIO

Look at the illustration above. Even though the models have the same torso measurement, the model on the left has short legs compared to the model on the right, who is visually balanced.

How to Measure Your Vertical Body

1. Measure from the top of your head to your leg/hip crease.

2. Measure from the your leg/hip crease to the floor.

If your legs appear to be longer than the top portion of your body, they are visually balanced. But if they appear equal to or shorter than the top portion of your body, you have short legs.

Are You Short-, Average-, or Long-Waisted?

Tie a string around your natural waistline. (You may need someone to help with measuring.)

1. Turn to the mirror and hold a yardstick behind your back at the top of your legs (as if you are sitting on it). Measure the length from the top of your legs to the string.

2. Place a yardstick across your shoulders from corner to corner. Measure the length from the string to your shoulders.

• You are **short-waisted** if your upper torso is shorter above the string.

• You are **average-waisted** if your upper torso is slightly longer above the string.

• You are **long-waisted** if your upper torso is distinctly longer above the string.

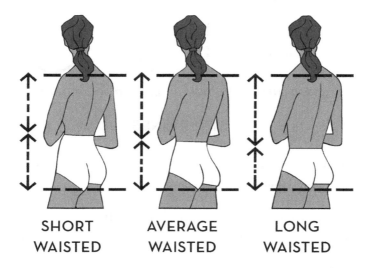

SHORT
WAISTED

AVERAGE
WAISTED

LONG
WAISTED

Now Take Inventory

Does your shoulder-to-hip ratio appear balanced, top-heavy, bottom-heavy?

What is your body shape? _____

What is your vertical body type:

- Do you have short legs or are you visually balanced? _____

- Are you short-waisted, average-waisted, or long-waisted? _____

You Are Who You Are

So you begin here, with the body you have now. Everyone has the ability to be a "shape shifter." How? By visually moving lines in clothing to create a pleasing silhouette. The idea is to balance your proportions, and balance begins with the eye, not the measuring tape.

How would you ultimately like to look? Taller, thinner, curvier, less curvy? Want to disguise your tummy, thighs, large hips? Read on.

HALF AND HALF

You may wear a Petite size for tops, but need a Misses size for bottoms, or vice versa. Try shopping in both Misses and Petite departments—one department for each half of your body.

Basic Lines

There are four basic style lines:

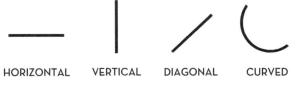

HORIZONTAL   VERTICAL   DIAGONAL   CURVED

STYLE LINES

1. **Horizontal Lines** move the eye from side to side. Wear them on parts of your body you want to widen or shorten.

2. **Vertical Lines** move the eye up and down. In general they make you look taller. Anything that makes you appear taller makes you appear thinner.

3. **Diagonal Lines** go across your body at an angle. The more vertical the diagonal line, the taller and slimmer you look. The more horizontal the diagonal line, the wider you look.

4. **Curved Lines** are very feminine and can enhance many figure types. Wear

them in areas you would like to accentuate or add volume. But beware: if you are already curvaceous, in the face or body, repeating a shape will emphasize it. (For example, circular earrings on an already-round face may make it appear even wider and rounder. Or a swirling pattern worn at your bustline can make your bosom appear larger.)

Clothing is made up of a visual assortment of these lines. The lines may either be structural lines sewn into the garment, or ornamental lines incorporated into the pattern. There are also lines created when one piece of clothing meets another piece of clothing on the body, for example, where the hemline of a jacket hits the pants. These are precisely the lines it is possible to manipulate to create a desired visual effect.

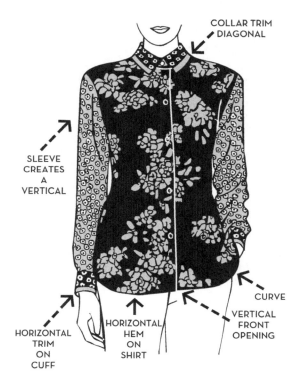

VISUAL LINES

So, if every garment is a collection of only four lines, and we are all a certain shape, our objective is to move the lines to attain our most flattering silhouette.

Keep in mind that the eye follows the direction of a line. Lines can visually move the eye at a faster or slower pace. Therefore, it is advantageous to speed the eye over parts of your body you want to camouflage. Likewise, you can slow the eye and call attention to areas you want to showcase.

- Solid and monochromatic outfits don't stop eye movement. They create one continuous look from head to toe. This is visually slimming.

- Curves (ruffles, peplum, lace, and pattern) slow the eye and bring emphasis to areas you want to draw attention to.

- Contrasting colors can chop up a look and slow down or even stop the eye.

SOLID COLOR VS. COLOR BLOCK

Fabric Weight

When choosing clothing, you should take the weight and texture of the fabric into consideration. Heavier textured fabrics can add visual weight to the body. They also tend to look more casual. Lightweight fabrics do not add visual weight and can be dressed up or down. For example, a cashmere sweater can be worn with jeans or a silk suit, but a cotton loose-weave sweater is probably too casual for a silk suit.

Certain bodies wear certain textiles better than others. Beware of thin, jersey-like knits if you are heavy or have soft bulges. Even with shape wear, this fabric may not be your best choice. You may need a lined or weightier fabric with more structure. And never be afraid to try a size larger (or smaller) for a better fit.

Proportion

Wearing clothing that is in alignment with your body's proportion is important when dressing. Oftentimes large women try to hide under loose, baggy clothing, but this only makes them appear more shapeless and perhaps even larger. Baggy clothes DO NOT . . . I repeat . . . DO NOT help us look slimmer. Plus-sized women should wear clothing that skims their bodies and is the appropriate weight. And using the aforementioned principles of line can help focus the eye right where you want it to go.

Top-to-bottom proportion should also be taken into consideration when dressing. If you are going to wear a flowing top, you should generally team it with a more form-fitting bottom, while loose palazzo pants usually look best paired with a more form-fitting top. If both top and bottom are loose and flowing, it may create the illusion that someone is heavier than she really is.

MOVING LINES

Did you realize the placement of your shoulder or handbag could make you look wider? For example, if you carry a large shoulder bag at hip level, it is visually extending your hipline. That's right. It actually makes you appear broader. So be strategic when choosing handbag styles. Opt for styles that allow you to lengthen or shorten your shoulder strap. Oftentimes, you can even tie a knot in the strap or double it up to shorten it.

Classic Styles

Some styles are considered classics because they are more universally flattering than others. Take the V-neck for example. For most women a V-neck extends the neckline, creating a longer, leaner look. (Note: there are exceptions to this rule. If you have a very pointed chin and wear a V-neck, the shape of your chin is actually emphasized.)

Your goal in dressing should be to strive for visual balance. A marriage made in heaven is when the lines of your outfit and the lines of your body come together to create the illusion you want.

Now that you know how to use classic line and design principles to create desired results, the same information can help you decide the most complementary makeup placement as well as give you ideas for selecting the most flattering hairstyles and accessories.

"A woman should be an illusion."

—Ian Fleming

VISUALLY BALANCING
YOUR FIGURE

To lengthen legs:
- Wear one color from waist to toe
- Wear garments with vertical lines from the waist down, such as: rows of vertical buttons, pants with creases, seams, etc.
- Shoes, stockings/socks, and pant hemline—same color

To balance wide hips and narrow shoulders:
- Wear shoulder pads, even if they aren't in style
- Vertical lines from the waist down will slim hips, while horizontal lines on upper torso will widen shoulders
- Add volume above the waist (epaulets, bateau neckline, wider lapels)

To elongate or thin a neck:
- Wear necklines open to or below the collarbone
- Wear hairstyles up or off the neck
- Avoid short necklaces and high, closed collars

To shorten a long waist:
- Wear high waistbands or belts that match the color worn below your waist
- Wear tops with horizontal necklines, yokes, horizontal stripes, or breast pockets

To lengthen a short waist:
- Wear belts in colors that match your top
- Wear contour belts that drop down below your waist
- Select tops with torso-lengthening vertical lines

To look more curvaceous (for flat derriere):
- Wear full skirts (gathered in back)
- Wear pants with hip pockets or embellishments on back pockets

To conceal large thighs and/or saddlebags:
- Wear full or A-line skirts
- Wear pants with plenty of thigh room rather than snug pants or pencil slim skirts
- Boot cut jeans with a slight flare give a balanced, slimming effect

To de-emphasize a wide waist:
- Select thin belts that match the color of the garment
- No belts with eye-catching or blingy buckles
- Wear semi-fitted jackets, unbuttoned
- If hips are slim, wear loose belts draped at an angle at hipbone level

To de-emphasize a protruding tummy:
- Avoid tight waistbands, spreading pleats, bulky, bias-cut (fabrics cut on the diagonal) or excessive fabric gathered at the waist
- Skirts flatter more than pants

To de-emphasize a protruding derriere or heavy buttocks:
- Tops should end slightly above or definitely below the plumpest part of the hip
- Skirts are usually more flattering than pants
- Long pants are usually more flattering than capris
- Avoid bias-cut and clinging fabric

∽ 5 ∽

Wardrobe ABCs

*"My mission in life is not merely to survive, but to thrive;
and to do so with some passion, some compassion,
some humor, and some style."*

—Maya Angelou

Have you ever been intimidated by women who seem to "have it all together" when it comes to their appearance? Are you consistently confident about your own style savvy, or do you doubt your ability when it comes to putting together smart-looking outfits? Simply buying new clothes is not the answer. Chances are good that you already have some excellent pieces in your closet. I tell my clients there are only three things you must know and do in order to have a well-engineered wardrobe.

Years ago, I wrote a book called *Build an INFINITE Little Wardrobe—Simple as ABC.* I came upon the idea when I saw people struggling in airports like beasts of burden with their excess luggage. What in the world were they carrying in there? I decided to design a system that would teach practical concepts and offer ideas for capsules of travel-friendly clothes. In my book, the acronym, A-B-C, stands for:

A Accessories in sets

B Bases

C Cordial colors

These three ideas are the foundation of a system that enables anyone to combine clothing and accessories for maximum versatility and personal style. Every time I shop with a client or go into someone's closet I teach these concepts. Increased confidence and ease of dressing is always my ultimate goal for them.

If you understand these three basic principles of wardrobe mechanics, you can save yourself thousands of dollars in purchasing mistakes. You will also save time and stress while shopping and dressing—which is infinitely more valuable. If you are a person who stands in your closet at length, wondering what to wear, and even after choosing you are still not convinced you look great, this information is essential for you. It is guaranteed to simplify dressing and ultimately amp up your self-confidence. And the good news is, the formula works every time! Yes, you read that correctly.

> **Style is all about combining clothing and accessories to create a one-of a-kind look that wholly and completely defines the individual.**

Begin to Think "Bases"

The key components to an infinite little wardrobe are base pieces.

Outside Bases

An outside base is a matching jacket and bottom (think typical suit), OR any third-layer piece and a bottom.

A third-layer piece can be a jacket or anything that works like a jacket; for example, a pashmina/wrap, sweater, poncho, hoodie, cardigan, vest, pullover, or lace tunic. It may be as tailored and corporate as a business suit or as casual as workout clothes.

So if you have a comfortable flattering pair of trousers or a skirt you wish you could wear every day, the first thing to add to your shopping list is a jacket/third-layer piece to match that favorite bottom. Then you can wear every single top you own (that does not clash in color and is of similar mood or style) with your newly created favorite outside base. Be sure to shop in your closet first.

MATCHING OUTSIDE BASE

THE POWER OF A JACKET

A jacket is unquestionably the number one garment *in the world* that connotes authority. A jacket is synonymous with "business." Even when powerful leaders appear *sans* tie at casual conferences and meetings, it is likely that they will wear jackets.

But you don't have to be a business professional to use the power of the jacket. A schoolteacher who wants to set a standard of discipline on her first day will wear a jacket. A homemaker who plans to run for the School Board may want to wear a jacket when attending a meeting or a luncheon. Anyone can appear more poised and self-assured simply by donning this third-layer piece.

And a third-layer piece always finishes a look, no matter what the occasion. Consider these options for third-layer pieces, listed from most formal to most casual:

- **Traditional suit**
- **Tailored blazer**
- **Unstructured jacket or cardigan**
- **Denim jacket**
- **Hooded jacket with workout clothes**

(Within each category, the darker the color the more authoritative the look.)

Whether part of a suit or worn alone, jackets immediately set a commanding tone and give the impression of credibility. I always recommend wearing a jacket or suit when interviewing, requesting a pay raise, or just giving an important presentation.

Throw a navy blazer in the back seat of your car, or hang it in your office. You never know when you may need your coat of armor!

Inside Bases

An inside base is a matching top and bottom. (A one-piece dress or a jumpsuit can also be considered an inside base.) An inside base becomes the platform for any additional third-layer piece.

Examples of inside bases:

- shirt/pants
- skirt/blouse
- jumpsuit
- shorts/tank top
- jeans/t-shirt
- basic one-piece dress

A great-fitting pair of black slacks and a black top can become your matching inside base. Now, stand at your closet and search for all the third-layer pieces that could coordinate with them (for example, a jean jacket, emerald cardigan, beige pullover, or vest).

MATCHING INSIDE BASE

The reason bases work is because when the base pieces (either inside or outside) match, the odd piece automatically becomes an accessory.

Begin by looking at the garments in your closet to see how many inside and outside bases you already own. You may not realize all the different ways you could team them with other things you have.

Orientation Tour

Whenever clients buy a new garment or accessory, the first thing I encourage them to do when they get home is to go to their closets and introduce the new to the old. I call this an orientation tour. "Wow" is the typical response I get. Clients are continually shocked at how many new outfits they can put together simply by using things they already own. The *fewest* number of new outfits I have ever discovered in all the years of refashioning a client's closet is 15.

If I am working in a closet, instead of simply asking my clients to *think* about clothing they can put together, I ask them to hold the garment on a hanger and *physically* move it alongside pieces they already own, passing it over each top and each bottom that is hanging there, to see how many new combinations can be made. Don't just visualize it, actually see it.

Try this: Go to your closet and search for matching tops and bottoms. Then add a third-layer piece (or set of accessories) you have never teamed with that inside base before. *Voilá...* new outfits all week long.

Accessories in Sets

A set of accessories is a combination of accessories that relate well to one another, either by color, mood, texture, style, or print. Together, these pieces make a good team and present a cohesive look. The items do not have to be the same color, although they can be (and this is probably the easiest way to pair them).

Your bases will become the stage for all your sets of accessories. Accessories may include jewelry, hair ornaments, hosiery, scarves, belts, shoes, hats, or bags, and even eyewear. Any embellishment that creates a focal point or transforms the mood of the outfit can be considered an accessory. Glance at these illustrations to see how the sets of accessories relate to one another.

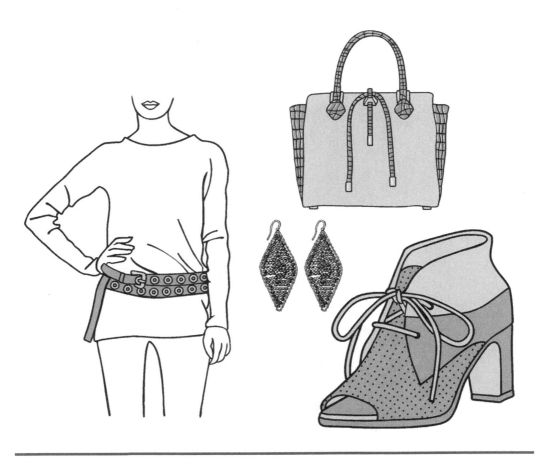

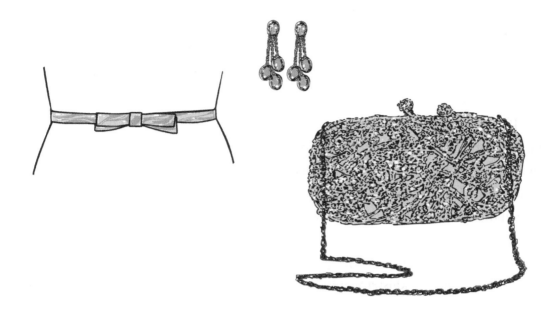

I recently met with a group of ladies who were astonished when I created seven different looks from one basic dress. The looks ranged from casual to dressy. (I used sets of accessories from my own closet. Some of them were at least 30 years old, still favorites of mine.) The reason every look was successful was because the accessories *go with me*, not because they go with the dress.

If an accessory is very "you," it will give you decades of wearing pleasure.

If you went to your closet right now, imagine how you might combine accessories you already own into sets. Since each piece was individually chosen by you, no one else is privy to it. Can you imagine how these sets could individualize your look by adding flair, polish, or even whimsy to your outfit? It wouldn't matter if someone were wearing a dress identical to yours—if you accessorized differently, the look would truly be your own. *That is signature style!*

Think back to images of Jacqueline Kennedy Onassis wearing her ubiquitous sheath dress. How lackluster would it have appeared if she had not teamed the dress with pearls, gloves, a pillbox hat, or a simple pair of sunglasses?

Can you imagine Grace Kelly without her chiffon scarves or signature handbag? How about Elizabeth Taylor *sans* her jewels? Each of these iconic women possessed such distinctive flair for accessorizing that her fashion imprint is still etched in memory today.

How much is considered *too much* when it comes to accessorizing? From my viewpoint as a stylist, accessorizing is a personal choice. As discussed earlier, comfort level, appropriateness, and intention all play key roles when it comes to fashion decisions.

I like to refer to accessories as "necessaries." And I happen to own more accessories than I do clothing. To me, clothing simply sets the stage—it is my canvas. Accessories create the real art.

COLOR 1 CAPSULE WARDROBE

When does 2 + 2 + 5 = 30?

When you combine 2 suits, 2 neck accessories,

and 5 blouses to get 30 different looks.

Yes really!

WHAT YOU NEED:

2 SUITS in SOLID CORDIAL COLORS
Examples of a suit:

- jacket/skirt
- pashmina/skirt
- jacket/slacks
- hoodie/yoga pants
- cardigan/jeans

May be an unmatched suit as long as the colors of the two pieces mix harmoniously.

2 NECK ACCESSORIES that match the bottom piece of each of the suits.
(For example: black slacks and black onyx necklace)

5 BLOUSES/TOPS
Examples:

- t-shirts
- button down shirts/blouses
- sweaters
- camis

Plain or patterned as long as they coordinate with both jackets and both bottoms.

Voilá . . . 30 different looks—20 with jackets and 10 without

ADD:

- 1 more skirt or slacks (in different, but harmonizing color)
- 1 more top
- 1 more accessory to match the new skirt or slacks

Now 54 different looks can be created.

> ## "BOTTOMS UP" RULE
>
> A relatively unknown concept known as "bottoms up accessorizing" is one of the easiest ways to pull an outfit together. It simply means wearing an accessory at your face (for example a scarf, bold pair of earrings and/or necklace, hair accessory, etc.) that is the same color as your slacks or skirt.
>
> If you wear jeans every day, a denim-colored necklace and/or earrings should be a "must-have accessory" for your wardrobe.

Cordial Colors

Cordial colors refer to those colors that look the most flattering on you. If one color looks good on you and another color looks good on you, theoretically you can combine the colors and they will look good on you together. (See Color Chapter)

Examples of some unique color combinations you may want to experiment with:

- Brown and pale blue
- Brown and turquoise
- Brown and navy
- Brown and black
- Navy and black
- Navy and turquoise
- Turquoise and orange
- Purple and orange
- Purple and red
- Purple and green

You can also mix prints and textures for instant interest. Try these unexpected pairings: denim/animal print, cashmere/chambray, leather/lace, sequins/denim, and tweed/silk.

Monochromatic Looks

Creating outfits using all one color or even different shades of the same color is one way to create an extremely sophisticated look.

If you find that your black tops and bottoms don't match exactly, the solution is to add more pieces of varying tones of black. That way the outfit looks intentional and transforms into a chic monochromatic look.

It is worth mentioning that monochromatic looks are also extremely slenderizing. (Especially from the rear view.)

THE ULTIMATE ACCESSORY

One of the most practical and flattering accessories you can own is a pair of earrings that match your eye color. They will instantly add brightness to your face by enhancing the color you already have in your eyes. And since the earrings go with *you*, rather than some specific outfit, they can be worn with anything.

Do you have eyes of blue, brown, hazel, or green? Give your face a double punch of color by adding earrings that match. Works every time!

"Everything that adorns a woman,
everything that serves to show off her beauty,
is part of herself . . ."

—Charles Baudelaire

Accessorizing Tips

- For new outfits, find a necklace or earrings to finish the look. (Shop your closet first.)

- Clear necklaces are even more versatile than silver or gold, and will go with any outfit.

- The key to a three-color combination is to repeat the bottom color near your neck.

- Not everyone is a "scarf person," just as some women prefer to wear classic gold or silver jewelry rather than color-coordinated or fashion jewelry.

- If you want to get more practice accessorizing in sets or adding to ones you already own, it costs you nothing to peruse displays at department stores. Style magazines are also a great source for ideas on creatively pairing accessories.

- Ask about store return policies. You can almost always purchase an accessory and take it home for an orientation tour. If it doesn't work out, take it back.

- Bold and tiny accessories can work together, such as tiny diamond studs paired with a bold statement necklace.

- Accessories don't have to match, they just have to relate well to each other or to the overall feel of the outfit. In other words, they don't have to be siblings, just "close cousins."

- If you are not wearing a necklace, wear larger statement earrings in a complementary color. I call this "ears only" accessorizing.

- Any color can be used as a neutral. The key to making it work is having enough pieces of the same color.

- Have fun with your accessories. Be yourself. Wear what makes you happy.

YOUR PERSONALITY PYRAMID

Your face is the communication center of your body. And I like to call the area between the top of your head and your shoulders "your personality pyramid."

Imagine yourself sitting behind a desk, or chatting at a table in a coffee shop, or even drinking cocktails at a bar. If you think about it, the head and shoulders are typically the only portions of our bodies that are on display, never mind those killer heels or that rhinestone belt.

I tell clients that the personality pyramid is the easiest place to create a focal point. Begin to think "head first" when you want to create a look. Use your hairstyle, makeup, and accessories to express your signature style.

Just imagine all the accessories that can bring complementary color to the face, create a mood for an outfit or simply add a bit of *je ne sais quoi* to the woman who is wearing them. Want to become mysterious, sensuous, playful, sophisticated? Simply transform your personality pyramid using earrings, necklaces, decorative collars, glasses, hair embellishments, makeup, scarves, or hats.

A jean jacket instantly "casualizes" an outfit. In the same way, pearls will always add sophistication and lace will create femininity. A portrait collar revealing a bit of décolleté will most decidedly increase the sexiness factor, and ravishing red lips can give you just the bombshell look you desire.

European women have been masters of manipulating the personality pyramid for ages. Their wardrobe may be limited to basic pieces, but it usually contains an abundance of accessories.

Decide what it is you want to communicate and experiment with your own personality pyramid. And remember: your crowning accessory should always be your smile.

PERSONALITY PYRAMID

∾ 6 ∾

Your Closet Is
A RIVER . . .

"It's not quantity that counts—it's workability."

–Janna Beatty

When I graduated from college, I took a job as a tour manager for travelers to the Holy Land. Years later, after I became an image consultant and consequently added closet makeovers to my list of client services, I often found when I walked into a muddled, overstuffed closet, the only metaphor that came to mind was: Your closet is a river, *NOT THE DEAD SEA!*

I consistently find that women (and men) bring loads of clothing, shoes, and accessories into their closets (usually slowly and over time), but never give a single thought to ever getting rid of anything. Your clothes were meant to flow through your closet like water passing through a stream. They shouldn't be held captive there for all eternity.

Imagine your closet—just as it is—at this very moment. Is it supporting your lifestyle? Do you consistently have what you need at your fingertips? Is it helping or hindering your ease of dressing? Do your clothes fit and flatter? Do you love wearing them? Do they bring you happiness?

I'm here to declare that your closet should be intimate and inviting. A space you can luxuriate in. After all, every garment occupying every precious square inch of your closet was carefully chosen *by you.* It didn't just wander in there by itself. Your wardrobe is your own *personal collection.* Do you think of it that way?

Most of the mistakes I find in peoples' closets are directly related to the purchase of a new outfit for an event happening "this Saturday night." Oftentimes a pressing deadline causes us to feel obliged to buy something new. So instead of sticking with a plan and taking time to shop for something we really love, we end up with a closet full of "one-night stand" outfits (and shoes) that choke the entire flow of our closets.

I believe our closets are true representations of our lives. Having a closet full of clothing that doesn't serve you only bogs you down. But before you can begin to revamp your closet, it is essential that you first realistically evaluate your lifestyle, the life you are living *today.*

Your Lifestyle

If there are 168 hours in a week, with approximately 56 of those hours being taken up by sleep, that leaves 112 remaining hours. What activities are you involved in during those 112 hours? Regardless of the specifics, most of us have general periods of work, leisure, and social engagements. On the graph below, create your own time pie, based on your specific routine. (It may be helpful to break down, in hours, time spent at each activity.)

1. _____ (hrs)   4. _____ (hrs)

2. _____ (hrs)   5. _____ (hrs)

3. _____ (hrs)   6. _____ (hrs)

Your Time Pie Graph

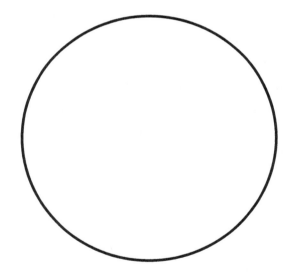

After you define and divide the sections of your pie, you can better survey the contents of your closet to determine whether the divisions in your pie match the clothing you need to support your lifestyle.

As stated earlier, I frequently work with clients who are going through some sort of transitional period in their lives. It is important to recognize as the seasons in our lives change, so does our pie, and so should our closets.

HAVE YOU HAD A LIFESTYLE CHANGE?

I find that many people do not have a clear view of their lifestyles. For example, one client of mine was a mother and wife whose husband had just been promoted to a prominent administrative position. Suddenly she was expected to attend formal functions several times each month (not each year, but each month). When I met her, she confessed that she was always scrambling to find stylish clothing to wear to these affairs.

In her own eyes, she still viewed herself as simply a busy mother. She had not stopped to consider her new role—that of a CEO's wife. Her time pie had changed. Now, one-fourth of her time was spent attending formal engagements with her husband. She needed one-fourth of her wardrobe designated for those occasions. Subsequently, one-fourth of her clothing allowance could now be allotted for more formal garments.

Once my client took into account her dual positions as both a mom and a professional's wife, she began to understand the importance of building a formal capsule wardrobe. This eased her anxiety about finding something suitable to wear at a moment's notice and helped her justify the cost, which she could now view as her own "business expense."

An important point this story illustrates is that we must continually reevaluate who we are and recognize the inevitability of change in our lives and our lifestyles.

I find that people are either weeders *or* keepers. Take your own "tour de closet." Can you easily access things you wear on a daily basis, or is your closet jam-packed with clothes you don't wear or haven't gotten rid of?

Is your closet organized in a way that affords you the simplicity and ease of dressing you deserve or is it out of control because you can't seem to part with anything? Here are some common excuses for *not* clearing out the clutter:

- I'm hoping to lose weight, and when I do, I can't wait to get into that outfit again!
- I can't possibly part with that. I spent way more than I should have on it.
- I've only worn that outfit once, I haven't gotten my money's worth out of it.
- I'm saving that in case I ever go back to work.
- I'm waiting for this to come back in style.
- This is the suit I wore on my wedding day.

Do any of the above statements sound like you?

To all these defenses, ask yourself:

- Is my closet a reflection of my lifestyle TODAY?

- Where would I wear this? (Do I own something that might look better?)

- How often would I wear it this season?

- Does this garment fit me NOW?

- Is this item still in fashion?

- Is it comfortable?

- Do I have what I need to wear with this garment to complete the outfit, including shoes?

Many people feel completely overwhelmed at the thought of reorganizing their closets. I remind clients that they deserve to look good *today*. I often give them permission to get rid of what is no longer functional or practical. Some people need positive affirmation that they can let go of past purchases or sentimental garments. These days memories can easily be stored in your camera, instead of your closet.

Below are some guidelines to help your closet become a flowing river, not just a stagnant sea of stuff.

"—clothes that never leave the closet are freeloaders."

–Kate Spade

Tips for Tackling Your Closet

The Golden Rule I give my clients during a closet intervention is:

HAVE NOTHING IN YOUR CLOSET THAT YOU CANNOT PUT ON AND WEAR RIGHT NOW!

That includes:

- Any garment that isn't in season now

- Any garment that doesn't fit now

- Any garment that needs pressing or repairs

It's important to look at your pie graph and consider what activities you are engaged in the majority of the time. Your closet should reflect that. For example if 50 percent of your 112 hours are spent working, 50 percent of your clothes should be for work. That means if you do not look appropriate at work, it may be time to spend your shopping dollars on these types of garments.

Be brutal when deciding what to keep and what to get rid of. But remember: in the long run, less is more, because fewer garments will free up your space so you can really see what you have. Consequently, you will wear your best pieces more frequently.

Simply by deleting garments, your closet will appear more organized, because you have created less visual clutter. By removing just a few things, you will be surprised at the results. Most of my clients say they "fall back in love" with their clothes, simply because they have found them!

What Should You Keep?

We've discussed clearing out clothing from your closet. Now here are some guidelines to help you decide when to hang on to something. Keep a garment or accessory if it is:

- Classic

- Fine quality

- A complementary color

- Great fitting

- Comfortable and flattering

- Not "tired" looking, i.e., it looks like new

Of course, space permitting, you can keep anything you want. But that doesn't mean you have to look at it on a daily basis if you're not wearing it now. If you have extra closets in other rooms, move out-of-season clothing there. If you are planning to lose weight, but just haven't lost it yet, move non-fitting clothing to another area and arrange it from the largest to the smallest size. That way, when you shed pounds, you can go shopping in your storage closet.

"Hanging on to a bad buy *will not redeem the purchase."*

–Sir Terence Conran

Organizing Your Private Collection

Once you have decided what to keep and what to move out, use these tips to help organize your space:

- Dressier clothes should hang toward the back of the closet (unless you wear them often)
- Pants hung together—casual to dressy
- Skirts hung together—casual to dressy
- Tops hung together—casual to dressy (sleeveless, short sleeve, long sleeve)
- Tops should also hang together by fabric type (knit, cotton, silk)
- Jackets and third-layer pieces together

There are no rules regarding the amount of clothing you should own. Whatever your space and lifestyle prescribe is the correct amount for you. However, I generally find the following ratio of tops to bottoms to jackets to be ideal:

1 Jacket (or third-layer piece)

to 3 Bottoms

to 5 Tops

I call this my **1 – 3 – 5 FORMULA**. Of course, this formula can vary from person to person. If you work behind a desk all day, most people will see your tops on a daily basis—thus you may want to have a greater variety. A woman in a very authoritative position would probably want to have more jackets in her closet. (Jackets also help hide a protruding tummy.) So think about your own individual situation and you can decide for yourself.

I have a client who likes a stress-free zen closet. Clutter confuses her, so she asks me to come twice a year and put together her outfits for a season. If something will not be worn that season, it is stored out of sight.

Customize Your Closet

When I think back to the very first apartment I ever had, I remember arranging my kitchen exactly the way my mother had always arranged hers. Even though my space was completely different, doing things in a familiar, conventional way seemed right. But sometimes the "tried and true" way isn't always the most efficient way.

When builders build closets, they usually rely on a standard unit of measure for constructing clothing racks and shelves. Most of us simply use the prescribed space to hang clothes and stack shoes where indicated. But what if you have a high hanging rack for dresses, but you hardly ever wear dresses? Or you have loads of hanging space, but no room to store the 200 pairs of shoes you own?

Instead of working with the generic layout the builder gave you, determine the main components of your wardrobe and adapt your closet to fit them. Here are some of my favorite ideas:

- Add a second hanging rack under the higher bar if needed.
- If you have room for an out-of-season rack in the back or near the ceiling, install it.
- Bring in more storage for shoes using shelving placed at intervals that actually reflect/fit your heel heights.
- My personal favorite idea is to install a spring tension rod for hanging necklaces.

Don't be afraid to test-drive storage devices. Some work and some don't. It depends on your space, your wardrobe, and your habits. My mantra is: IF YOU CAN'T SEE IT, YOU WON'T USE IT! We don't wear what we can't see, so try to have clothing, shoes, and accessories in full view, not hiding away in opaque containers or pretty jewelry boxes.

Once you begin to examine your closet's potential, you can come up with your own solutions to individualize and improve the function of your space. The hard work you put into a more organized system for dressing will pay off by saving you time and money. And ultimately you will gain a newfound confidence from looking undeniably put-together.

More Practical Closet Ideas

- Transform a blank wall in your closet or bedroom into a "staging area" for you to lay out clothing, accessories, and shoes so you can *rehearse* an outfit. Perhaps you have seen styling grids in the dressing rooms of your favorite department stores. These grids allow you to hang and move garments easily to create different looks.

- A full-length mirror is a must-have for every closet. If you don't have room in your closet for a mirror, make sure it is in close proximity to your dressing area. There is no way to see how your entire outfit looks without one, and it absolutely has to be full-length.

- Put a pad and pencil in your closet, so you can keep a running list of items you need to replace or purchase in order to complete an outfit. I take my list with me when I shop. This helps me avoid overbuying and repeat buying, and stay focused on what I really need.

- If you want to keep the size of your wardrobe as it is, take out one garment for every new garment you bring in. To *decrease* the size of your wardrobe, take out two/three garments for every new one you bring in.

- Even after you've revamped your closet, you can't expect it to stay organized if you don't take time regularly to tidy it up. By hanging garments promptly after wearing or placing soiled clothing in a hamper and putting clean laundry away in a timely manner, you can be assured of maximum functionality and ease of dressing. This is all part of good closet management. (If you aren't careful, your closet could very quickly return to the quagmire it once was.)

- The amount of money you spend on clothes should be directly proportionate to the time you spend wearing them. For example, if you spend 40 percent of your time working, 40 percent of your wardrobe allowance should be devoted to work clothes. The same goes for casual, sporty, or formal clothes. Spend your dollars where you spend your time.

- Take stock of your closet. Are you harboring items there that are not related to dressing? This is your inner sanctum, a refuge where you have the opportunity to refresh and recreate yourself every day. If scrapbooks, toys, china, or other miscellaneous items are taking up prime real estate in your closet, find another home for them.

Have fun transforming your closet into your own amazing fashion boutique.

Years ago, I had a senior client with quite exquisite taste. She had not taken stock of her closet in years. It was packed to the gills. I don't even think *she* knew what was in there! She simply couldn't bear to part with anything. The reason: she was terrified that one day she might need something and it wouldn't be there.

The problem was not only too much clothing, but an emotional attachment to the clothing. My solution would have to involve both managing the quantity of clothing while alleviating her fear of losing anything.

On the day of the closet overhaul, I brought over several large packing boxes with hanging racks. I also brought my "tough gal" approach.

Knowing she was not mentally prepared (so she thought) to part with the clothes, I suggested she store all the garments and accessories she had not worn for the last year in the boxes provided. We would then move the boxes to her garage. She was free to go and retrieve anything she wanted from her "box wardrobe" at any time.

But there was one stipulation to this plan. If, after one year, she had not opened a box, she would have to get rid of it, without even so much as looking inside. She agreed.

Only a few weeks later, my lovely client called to say that she had already donated every box in her garage to a local charity. "Oh, Janna," she said, "it happened just like you said it would—and I didn't need a year to figure it out!"

Not only had she decluttered her closet, but she had also discovered forgotten clothing and accessories and fallen back in love with them.

~ 7 ~

Shopping:
CREATING YOUR PERSONAL COLLECTION

"Women usually love what they buy,
yet hate two-thirds of what is in their closet."

—Mignon McLaughlin

Why do some women *love* to shop and others *hate* it? Most likely because they have either been very successful or very unsuccessful at it. People are reluctant to repeat something if there is no payoff, only frustration.

According to Retailwire.com, the top 10 reasons women hate to shop for clothes are:

- Lack of awareness of what looks good on them
- Busy lifestyles
- Shopping is no longer needed for socialization
- Difficulty staying on top of fashion trends
- Overwhelmed
- Disorganized
- Dissatisfied with their weight
- Guilt—they don't feel comfortable spending on themselves
- Ineffective sales associates
- Some even enjoy saying they "don't like to shop"

If your shopping history has been less than ideal, begin now to consider some of these potential pitfalls:

Common Shopping Mistakes

- You buy clothes according to size, not fit. Standardization of size no longer exists. REMEDY: Try a variety of sizes. If you are in a hurry and can't try clothes on, shop with a string that you have pre-measured at bust, waist, hips, etc.
- You didn't have a plan for the future of the outfit (or shoes), so now it's a "lone wolf" taking up valuable space in the back of your closet. Most superfluous clothing purchases are made because the buyer had to have something spur of the moment to wear. REMEDY: Look for pieces you can pair with something you

already own. For example, a knit jersey dress can be amped up with pearls and high heels, or "casualized" with a jean jacket and boots.

- You see someone wearing a knockout ensemble, ask them where they got it, and go buy the same thing. OR, you see a mannequin wearing something that looks luscious (things always seem to look luscious on mannequins) and promptly get the same outfit in your size. REMEDY: Don't assume an outfit will look the same on you as it does on your friend (or a perfectly proportioned plastic mannequin).

- You buy something on sale, simply because it was a good deal. REMEDY: Ask yourself how often you plan to wear the item and if it will coordinate with other pieces in your wardrobe. Test yourself to see if you are a "sale shopper" by looking in your closet. If there are outfits that still have price tags on them, you may be guilty. Buying on sale is practical in theory, but if the clothing is never worn, you've totally defeated your purpose.

Now that you have identified some of the hazards of shopping, hopefully you can move on to a more positive experience.

INFORMATION FOR
SAVVY SHOPPERS

Fashion professionals are aware of the best times to buy certain items of clothing, hit sales, and find the newest seasonal trends. Here are a few secrets from the industry.

- The best *shopping days* are early in the week.
- The best *shopping times* are early in the day. This is when stores are less crowded and you get more attention from sales associates.
- The exception to the aforementioned rule is to *shop for shoes later* in the day when your feet are at their plumpest.
- Major clothing sales occur two times a year, January and July.
- Fashion season begins in September, and spring fashions arrive just before Easter.
- Some garments are easier to find at specific times of the year. Try to shop for items you need when they are in season. For example, jackets are readily available before Easter, but usually don't appear again until September.
- Matching jackets, skirts, and trousers may be harder to find at discount or outlet stores because some pieces may have already been sold at the store where they originated. Consequently, you may not find as many pieces to choose from. So if you are looking for matching bases and third-layer pieces, you may have more luck shopping at department stores where selections are best.

Shopping Modes

Did you realize that there are very different approaches to shopping? Are you a shopper or a buyer, or both? Let's explore various styles of shopping. Once you've identified your approach, you can decide whether it's the most constructive one.

Recreational Shopping: This type of shopping, oftentimes done with family or friends, can lead to impulse buying. It's easy to get caught up in a spending spree if everyone else is doing it. Buying for "fun" can leave you with a closetful of superfluous items and a credit card full of superfluous charges. I tell clients, "Shop with a friend, but buy alone."

Retail Therapy: Shopping because you are bored, depressed, or upset? Usually unwanted purchases occur because you think buying something will help you feel better. Retail therapy isn't too dangerous if you limit your spending to inexpensive treats, such as lipstick, nail polish, or a new scarf.

Sensible Shopping: Searching stores for the newest trends, the lowest prices, and the best variety is a good idea *before* actually buying. This may take more time, but ultimately results in the best quality purchase for the money. Most stores will hold garments for a day or so. This gives you time to decide if you really want to buy.

Sensible shopping also allows you the opportunity to try on a garment at the store to examine the item for fit, color, quality, etc. If you decide you like it, you may want to check online to find a better deal on the same item.

First Things First

The first place to shop is in YOUR OWN CLOSET. No doubt you already have lots of great items. Ask yourself what it would take to remix or update ensembles using what you already own in your current collection.

If you have recently organized your closet, you may have discarded basic items that were worn, outdated, or no longer your current size. Keep an ongoing "needs list" for items you plan to purchase.

Your goal is to have an outfit and accessories in your closet that is ready to wear, for any event, at a moment's notice. If you have a basic capsule wardrobe (1 jacket/3 bottoms/5 tops), ideally you should be able to go to your closet at any time and select something appropriate to wear no matter what the occasion.

*"I love shopping.
There is a little bit of magic found in buying something new."*

—Rebecca Bloom

Let's Go Shopping

As previously mentioned, there are a myriad of reasons shopping may not have been the most pleasant of scenarios. Here are some ideas, even for the most seasoned shoppers, that can help save time and money and give you confidence to purchase with conviction.

First and foremost, set goals and be specific about what you need to buy. You probably take a list with you to the grocery store. Likewise, you should carry your wardrobe "needs list" with you. I keep a notepad in my closet and a duplicate list in my purse, since I never know when I might need to refer to it.

Head straight to the department where the item(s) you need can be found. It's easy to get distracted by all the lovely merchandise around you. Try to focus on the task at hand.

Allow yourself plenty of time. It takes a while to peruse the racks and try on clothes leisurely. If you don't allow enough time, you may get frustrated and end up buying something you don't really love, or perhaps nothing at all.

Be sure to carry snacks, water, or whatever else you need to sustain you for the duration of the trip. One client of mine is a diabetic and it is necessary for her to take provisions on a long shopping jaunt.

In the Dressing Room

Consider the following when deliberating the purchase of any garment:

1. Does the color complement my face and eyes?

2. Is the fit flattering/right for my size NOW?

3. Is the fabric in the garment an appropriate weight?

4. Does the garment have the structure I need for my figure type?

5. Is it practical for my lifestyle?

6. Is it worth the cost?

7. Is the garment machine washable or will it have to be dry-cleaned?

8. Do I have the appropriate undergarments to wear with it?

9. Do I own accessories and shoes to coordinate with the outfit?

10. Do I feel joy when I put this on? Is it me?

Don't overthink the clothing, but do trust your visceral (gut) reaction when you see it on.

Walk a few feet away from the mirror when you are trying on an outfit. Turn and take a sudden look back. If the clothing is too bright/contrasting, you will see the clothing first, not your face. Don't let your outfit overpower you.

And never be afraid to:

- **Try it on.** A garment might not appeal to you on the hanger, but it can take on new life when you try it on your body.

- **Think outside the box.** Do twist and turn the garment when you try it on. If the zipper is on the side of a skirt, experiment with how differently it would look if you turned the zipper to the back.

- **Go "out of your comfort zone."** How about leather pants, a fur vest, stilettos, or funky boots?

- **Look at yourself from every angle.** If there is a three-way mirror, make sure you position yourself so you can see all views. Yes, even the rear view!

- **Test drive a garment.** Bend, reach, sit, and squat in the clothes. Make sure they don't gap, pull, or ride up in the wrong places. I call this my GAP TEST.

More Shopping Tidbits

- Wear one of your favorite, best-looking outfits when you shop. This establishes a high standard of comparison, so your wardrobe gets better and better instead of just bigger and bigger.

- Get to know sales associates. You will discover the ones who have the most knowledge and once they get to know you, they'll be better able to direct you to the styles/designers you prefer.

- Before buying, try on or look at more expensive clothing. Notice details such as fit, lining, and draping of the material. Then attempt to imitate that look within the confines of your own budget.

- Familiarize yourself with the store's return policy. If you don't have time to try things on, or the lighting is bad, you may want to purchase the garment and try it on at home.

- Begin to discover your favorite designers and brands. If one designer's jeans fit and flatter you perfectly, why waste time trying others on? Cuts and sizing will vary from brand to brand.

- If you have trouble making complete outfits, shop less often but buy more pieces that harmonize with what you already own. This multiplies wardrobe versatility.

- Stay away from colors and lines that do nothing for you. It may look stunning on the mannequin, but if it doesn't flatter you with color and line, why waste your time?

- Ask yourself if it is more constructive to shop alone or with someone else. You can usually tell when a friend or relative is being honest, or just trying to be positive. Objective opinions from trusted sales associates may be more constructive. And, ultimately, you can always trust the mirror. I tell my clients, *"Never ask for an opinion unless you are willing to reject it!"*

- Do buy online, but beware of return policies. Do returns have free shipping? Is there a time limit to return?

- Consider cost per wear. A $10 t-shirt may initially seem like a good deal, but if it has to be replaced after only three or four washes because of shrinkage or fading, a higher-quality $25 t-shirt will ultimately end up being a better investment.

- Have a clear notion of who you are and the impression you want to give *today*. Refer to your time pie and recognize the cost of your clothes should be relative to the time you spend wearing them.

One of the many things I admire about my cherished daughter-in-law is an amazingly keen gift for discernment. She sets the bar extremely high when judging for quality. Before making any major purchases, clothing or otherwise, she asks herself the following questions:

"Am I longing for it?"

"Will my heart hurt if I walk away from it?"

If only we could all be this thoughtful and discriminating when selecting clothing. Our closets, instead of overflowing with mediocre outfits, would be filled with garments we truly adore!

∽

WHAT CAN A PERSONAL SHOPPER DO FOR YOU?

Spending just one afternoon with a Personal Shopper can be a phenomenal investment. If you purchase 15 pieces of clothing that will make 72 outfits, and you discover how to put garments together with ease and confidence every time you walk to your closet, your time and money have been well spent.

It is not my goal to shop *for* my clients; it is my goal to *coach* them on what works and what doesn't. I help them locate wardrobe pieces that fit their age, shape, and lifestyle, while always taking their personal coloring and individual preferences into consideration.

My goal is to "demystify" the shopping experience. And when I read a person's body language and see them grow right before my eyes, I know they have hit it correctly.

~ 8 ~

Let's Face It . . .
IT'S ALL ABOUT
THE SKINCARE

*"Today is the oldest you've ever been,
and the youngest you'll ever be again."*

—Eleanor Roosevelt

Mirror, mirror . . .

"When you look in the mirror, if you could change three things about your skin what would they be?" That is the primary question I ask clients when they come to me for skincare advice. I usually have my own ideas about their needs, but I always encourage them to voice their concerns first. They can usually pinpoint very quickly things they would like to change. But when I follow up by asking what they actually like about their skin, I almost always get a blank stare.

Photographs of women in magazines with practically perfect skin bombard us at every turn. How can the average woman possibly compete with an ever-present barrage of airbrushed beauties? And comparing ourselves to our "past selves" can be just as detrimental.

"Wrinkles show highlights of the soul's journey
through a lifetime."

—Rose Rosetree

We must realistically ask ourselves what can be improved. I believe practically any skin problem can be improved, and you are closer to attaining beautiful skin than you may think.

Just like your fingerprint is one-of-a-kind, so is your skin. My goal is to help clients understand their individual skin type and how to care for it. After you gain knowledge about your unique concerns, you can make the most informed decisions about products that are best for you. As a result, you will never fall prey to marketing ploys or become a victim of high-pressure sales people.

If you have a skin challenge, what's really going on is that your skin is *out of balance.* Your job is to become a "skin sleuth"—first by identifying the problem, then by attempting to pinpoint the cause. There can be any number of reasons for skin imbalance, and oftentimes the trouble may be based on something as simple as:

- Changes in makeup or skincare products
- Laundry detergent
- Hormones
- New medications/change in diet
- Changes in activity level
- Weather

One teen client of mine was having trouble with acne flare-ups. We discovered it was due to her frequent cell phone usage. She repeatedly placed the phone in the same spot on her face every time she used it. As a result, that area had become contaminated with bacteria and oil.

Begin by becoming your own skin sleuth. Investigate. Go down the list. Have you made any changes to your regular routine? Added or deleted new medications? If so, try changing one variable at a time to see if there is improvement/resolution.

Of course, the gene pool could always be the culprit. Skin texture, pore size, ultra dry skin, or under eye circles passed down from previous generations can be a challenge. But never fear: with advances in skincare products, you can improve just about any skin situation.

Once the cause of your problem has been determined, a customized routine can be established to get your skin back into balance. Then a systematic regimen can be adopted that will *keep* skin healthy and at its best. It's important to understand that if something is working, your skin will always let you know.

WHO IS THE STRANGER IN THAT PHOTOGRAPH?

A client of mine recently returned from a weeklong vacation. As she showed me photos of her trip, she dismally remarked, "I feel like I never look good in pictures these days. Sometimes I hardly recognize myself anymore!"

I explained that every day you see a familiar reflection of yourself in the mirror. But mirrors actually *reverse* your image. So what you see in the mirror is not what others see.

A camera captures an accurate depiction of your image. But since you are used to seeing yourself (reversed) in the mirror, a photograph may look askew.

On top of that, according to renowned face reader (physiognomist), Rose Rosetree, over the years, "Asymmetry happens. In fact . . . it is the single most universal way our face changes over time."

It boils down to this: Between the slight changes in our facial features resulting from gravity and age, *plus* a reverse image in the mirror—no wonder we see an imposter in our photographs!

Try this experiment:

- Place an earring on your left ear only.
- Stand in front of a mirror. Using your cell phone, take a photo of your reflection.
- Now turn your camera on yourself and take a "selfie."
- Compare the two photos. See how the first image is the reverse of the second?

A System

I have found that the best way to achieve optimal skincare results is to follow a 4 or 5-step regimen. But regardless of the number of steps, or the price you pay for products, *consistency* is the real key to dramatic improvement. You must be willing to invest time, effort, and money into your skin. When I say money, I don't mean using the most expensive products. You can achieve good results, whatever your budget. The key is knowing exactly what your skin requires.

Why a *system* and not just one or two products? Well, when you go to the gym, do you work out only your bicep muscles? Probably not, because the goal isn't simply to have great biceps, the goal is the health of the entire body. It's the same with your skin.

If you only cleanse and moisturize, chances are you aren't addressing other issues (lines, redness, breakouts, etc.) that contribute to the overall look and health of your skin.

You may be asking, *"Why should I spend so much time and energy on skincare when I can just camouflage my imperfections with makeup?"* The answer is simple. Makeup *always* looks better on healthy skin. Healthy skin is beautiful skin—and beautiful skin never goes out of fashion. It is also very difficult to fully cover imperfections. The more imbalanced the skin—whether it's from breakouts, large pores, wrinkles, etc.—the more textured and rough it appears. And caking on foundation and powder only magnifies the problem.

The five steps I recommend for ultimate skin health are:

1. Cleanse/Mask (using a freshener/toner is optional)
2. Hydrate
3. Moisturize
4. Repair
5. Protect

You can even combine some of these steps.

"Lifestyle Skincare" is what I call customizing a client's skincare program to fit her specific needs. Because, let's face it, if a regimen is too tedious, there's no way you will keep it up.

I make it a point to tell clients that it is not necessary to purchase products exclusively from one skincare line. Some women prefer to buy all their products from a particular line simply for convenience (and cosmetic companies like to market products that way), but never hesitate to change brands if you are not getting the results you want. It is more important to use what works, and use it consistently.

Five Steps to Beautiful Skin

Cleanse

I recommend cleansing twice a day. Select a cleanser that appropriately supports your particular skin type, whether it be dry, sensitive, combination, oily, acne-prone, etc.

But spend the least amount of money here, because cleansers are simply emulsifiers, meant to break down and remove residue and makeup.

I suggest using a daily cleansing mask (designed for your skin type) in the morning in lieu of a cleanser. The mask will gently exfoliate and polish skin and prepare the surface for makeup. Use your cleanser at night.

If you wash your face, and it feels tight, you are using the wrong cleanser. A client once came to my studio and after washing with the appropriate cleanser was amazed that her face "didn't hurt." I explained that your face should never feel pulled or tight after cleansing.

Never scrub. When you scrub your face, you are damaging your skin. The redness is proof. The top sixteen layers of your skin are the thickness of a tissue, so it is very easy to tear. As we mature, our skin thins even more.

When at-home dermabrasion kits first came out, I could look across a crowd and pinpoint every person who had used one. I am regularly astonished by people who don't recognize the damage they are inflicting on their skin by using sloughing sponges and hand-held brushes. There are gentler ways of achieving the look of polished skin rather than scrubbing it off. Thick, strong, young skin is less damaged by this aggressive brushing process, but the damage shows up in the future. If you want to exfoliate, it is more beneficial in the long run to use a mask. A mask gently exfoliates without being harsh.

Using a freshener or toner after cleansing may or may not be a part of your regular regimen. I specifically recommend using a freshener (for your specific skin type) if:

- your face doesn't feel totally clean after washing
- your makeup doesn't seem to last throughout the day
- your makeup tends to change color after you apply it

EYE MAKEUP REMOVER

The important thing to remember about eye makeup remover is that it should never contain oil, fragrance, or color. The poreless soft tissue under your eye cannot absorb, so these irritants can travel quickly into your eye.

Mask

Many women do not realize the purpose of masking, nor do they know how often to mask. I recommend daily masking, because it helps lift off dead skin-cell debris and preps the skin for moisturizer and foundation. Apply a cleansing mask and leave it on for a few minutes in the morning, in lieu of a cleanser.

There are a variety of masks designed to help with specific skin issues:

1. Hydrating/moisturizing
2. Tightening & firming/anti-aging
3. Calming
4. Exfoliating
5. Deep cleansing/purifying

You and you alone must determine your specific needs. And do not hesitate to use different masks on different areas of your face—even at the same time. (For example, a clay-based mask for an oily T-zone area, and a calming mask for the rest of your face.) Trust your skin to show you what treatment gives you the best results.

Hydrate

There is a common misconception in the skincare world that hydrating is the same thing as moisturizing. Hydrating refers to *plumping the skin with water.* (Imagine a raisin plumped up after it has been left in liquid.) Have you ever noticed a baby's skin? It's soft because it has a very high water content. As skin matures, it thins and its capacity to hold water decreases.

Hydrated skin retains moisture longer. That is why applying body lotion immediately after you shower, when your skin is still damp, is advised. This helps seal in hydration.

I am a proponent of electrolyzed/oxidized (EO) water. EO water has been used extensively in the Far East for years. When EO water is spritzed on the face and body, it plumps the cuticle of the skin and helps skin maintain moisture, while also forcing out impurities.

I spray EO water on my face, neck, and body. I suggest spritzing it on immediately after you cleanse (or mask), then follow with a moisturizer and foundation.

> ## WHAT IS EO WATER?
>
> Electrolyzed Water (also known as electrolyzed oxidized water) is ionized water that has been "restructured" into smaller units to provide better penetration of cells. In this way, it hydrates the skin at a cellular level, rather than merely at the surface. EO water is absorbed quickly and supplies additional moisture to skin.

Moisturize

Moisturizers are formulated differently. The first ingredient in most moisturizers is usually water. They are designed to treat primarily the top layer of the skin. But with advances in product formulations, some moisturizers are engineered to penetrate more deeply. And more emollient products, such as night creams, contain oil and are intended to increase skin's flexibility.

The thickness of your skin determines how well you retain moisture. Thick skin will hold moisture longer, while thinner skin holds less moisture and has more trouble retaining it. I use the example of a kitchen sponge compared to a sheet of tissue paper. It is easy to see which one will dry out faster.

> ### EYE CREAM
>
> Pat eye cream along the top of the cheekbone, never on the delicate skin directly under your eye. And if something is not formulated for the eye area, don't put it there.

Skin that has not been exfoliated has a harder time absorbing moisture efficiently, because the residue of old cells has not been sloughed off and can create a barrier on the skin's surface.

It is always important to use a moisturizer designed for your specific skin type. Even oily skin needs moisture. Choose one that is oil-free. (Tip: no need to moisturize your nose.)

Anything from travel, humidity levels, hormones, etc., can affect our skin's moisture needs. And as we mature, it may be necessary to add or change formulations.

Repair

Repair products refer to those products designed to remedy some type of skin problem or damage. Specific ingredients interact with skin cells in specific ways. It can be confusing because, depending on which skincare line you use, similar ingredients may be called by different names.

If you are not happy with some aspect of your skin, refer to the chart at the end of this chapter. It can help you determine which repair product(s) might be right for you. But it is only a guide. You may need to consult a skincare professional if problems persist.

Protect

Protecting your skin is the final step in a total skincare regimen.

Using foundation, or makeup base, is the best way to create a barrier between your skin and the damaging elements in the environment, because the pigment used in makeup foundations acts as an opaque shield of protection.

An experiment was done in New York City where women covered half their face with makeup base and left the other half bare. At the end of the day, they cleansed their skin and the residue was evaluated. The side of the face that was covered with foundation was actually cleaner than the side left bare. Why? Because the foundation acted as a buffer, protecting skin from the dirt and debris of the atmosphere.

Refer to Chapter 9 for more information on the benefits of using foundation, not just to look good, but also to protect your skin.

Now that you have become a more informed skin expert, when you speak with a sales associate at the cosmetic counter, you can confidently ask the following questions:

- "What are the active ingredients in the product?"
- "What does this active ingredient do?"

- "What results or changes can I expect to see in my skin when I use this product?
- "How soon can I expect results?"

If you want to test a product at home, do what I do and use it on only one side of your face. Do you see any changes? Can you feel a difference? Once again, your skin should tell you if a product is working or not. Another way to gauge effectiveness is to observe your face in the mirror before using the new product. For the next few days use the product, but don't scrutinize your skin. After several days, closely examine your skin to see if you are achieving the desired results.

My job is to teach clients how to understand their own skin, so they can thoughtfully consider what they need. Every product you purchase should serve you. It is important, as a consumer, to know that you have the right to return items that don't work for you. Ask about return policies before you buy.

Don't be pressured into making "prestige purchases" when it comes to skincare and makeup. Fancy packaging and endorsements by celebrities are fine but, ultimately, you are paying for that. There are plenty of reasonably priced, effective products that can give you good results without the *prestigious* price.

I get asked a myriad of questions on skincare. One client, who also happens to be a busy mom, recently wanted my thoughts on using facial cleansing wipes. I admitted they weren't my favorite. But I was quick to add, "If you find you are too tired to thoroughly cleanse your face at night, it's better to use a packaged wipe rather than not cleanse at all." (Just make sure they are formulated for your specific skin type.)

Keep in mind that good skincare is all about consistency. And consistency is always more achievable if you have a skincare routine that *fits your individual lifestyle.* But regardless of the number of steps in your routine, the objective of good skincare is to help you look and feel better. If you forego a step now and then, don't beat yourself up. Just feel good about what you can do.

Skin Problem/Solution Chart

Problem(s)	Possible Causes	Possible Solution	Product/Active Ingredient
Enlarged pores Fine lines	Accumulation of dead skin cells	Exfoliation	Cleanser with exfoliant Exfoliating mask
Dull skin	Lack of hydration	Spray skin with (EO) water	Electrolyzed/oxidized water
Dry skin	Loss of moisture Age	Moisturize	Moisturizer w/hyaluronic acid (holds moisture)
Loss of elasticity Aging lines Brown spots (hyperpigmentation)	Age Sun damage	Repair products containing:	Firming serums Alpha hydroxy acid Vitamin C
Blemishes	Age Hormones	Products containing:	Salicylic acid Benzoyl peroxide
Redness Inflammation Broken capillaries	Reaction to product, rash Rosacea Skin damaged by over-scrubbing Sensitive skin	Calming mask or products containing:	Allantoin Chamomile St. John's Wort
Eye puffiness Dark circles "Crow's feet"	Excessive sodium Lack of sleep Age	Eye products containing:	Caffeine Chamomile extract Green tea extract Ginkgo biloba extract
Oily skin	Genetics Age Hormones	Do not over–cleanse or dry out skin Do not scrub Use products containing:	Salicylic acid Lactic acid Copper sulfate Aloe
Lack of firmness	Age	Moisturizers & firming products containing:	Vitamins B, C, or E

The aging process only accounts for about 5% of damage to our skin. Most everything else is related to genetics, the environment (including sun exposure), and/or neglect.

~ 9 ~

Makeup
DESIGN

"Makeup is the final accessory."

—Janna Beatty

I must admit, the majority of my clients request a session on makeup design before they come in for a skincare consultation. But there is a reason the chapter on skincare precedes this one. Taking good care of your skin must *always* come first and must *never* be underestimated. *Beautiful skin, even with poor makeup application, still looks good. But rough, blemished, unhealthy skin (even with makeup) can never look its best.*

My clients are always quite shocked at how different they look after just one makeup design session with me. It is not because I am a great makeup artist, it's because I teach principles of light and shadow to create optical illusions that enhance the positive and camouflage features they don't love.

It is this illusion that can help anyone look more youthful. To understand *how* we can look younger, we must first identify two things that occur naturally during the aging process that cause us to *look older*: **loss of moisture** and **loss of color.**

So what can we do to reverse the ravages of time? Plastic surgery? Injections? Fillers? I believe there are less drastic and more effective ways to balance out the years by (1) replenishing moisture, and (2) adding color to create a more energetic version of ourselves.

The analogy I like to use is this: If I have two flowers on my desk, one picked this morning and the other picked yesterday, both look much the same. But on closer inspection, the flower picked earlier would probably be lighter in color and perhaps withering on the edges. The newly picked flower contains more color and moisture, which is vital to helping it appear fresh.

The previous chapter stressed the absolute importance of following a daily skincare regimen. If you are consistently moisturizing and rehydrating, you should be reaping rewards for your diligence: your healthiest, best skin possible. This skin becomes a blank canvas for color that will create a more vibrant-looking you.

I will pretend that you have just come to my studio for a makeup consultation. My aim is to help you understand different products and their uses. Then you can act as an informed consumer and choose which products work best for you and your lifestyle.

MY "FALL OFF" POINT

When I started my business over 30 years ago, it dawned on me that I could teach women how to age gracefully, and when it was my turn, I could pull out all my anti-aging tips and use them myself.

Well, a time came when I began to notice that my *ugly* days—you know, we all have them now and then—were beginning to outnumber my *pretty* days. But for the life of me, I wasn't able to figure out why. Somehow I couldn't quite manage to make myself look as good as I once had, even though I was putting in more and more effort.

In the Color 1 system, everyone can wear neutrals if they are the "right" neutrals, and I wore *a lot* of neutrals. But I had gotten to a point where my skin, eyes, and lips were looking faded. When nothing in my bag of tricks seemed to help me regain that fresh, energized look, that's when I took action and began to add more color to my face, hair, and wardrobe. And it worked!

The same situation happened to a lovely 50-something client of mine. One day she confided, "It's not my age that bothers me, Janna. It's walking into a room and feeling *invisible*." She was as slim and active as ever, so she couldn't quite pinpoint what had changed. She was ready to resort to injections and fillers to regain her youthfulness. That's when I told her my story.

Gradually, over time, pigment in our lips and our complexions begins to diminish. I refer to this natural occurrence as a "fall off" point. But even though our color may be fading, we certainly don't have to. We can rejuvenate ourselves by bringing color to our face and moisture to our skin.

When we realize the inevitability of change, we can take steps to do something about it.

Makeup Primers

A makeup primer works on your face like a ridge filler works on your fingernails. It floats over the skin and creates a smooth, flawless surface on which to apply your foundation. You can oftentimes get a sheerer, more natural look using a primer. Primers are available for all skin types and some even help increase the staying power of your foundation.

If you are wondering whether you are a candidate for makeup primer, simply place the primer on one side of your face and not the other. Follow with foundation as usual and check it immediately and then throughout the day. You can be the judge as to whether you look better with or without it.

Concealers

The main purpose of concealer is to cover skin imperfections (dark circles, blemishes, redness, etc.). Choose a concealer that is one shade lighter than your natural skin tone.

I even recommend concealers for my youngest clients when necessary, if they are prone to breakouts. They can use a formula containing acne-fighting ingredients such as salicylic acid, which is designed to treat blemishes while it hides them.

I prefer to use a brush to apply concealer, because you can paint it exactly where you need it. I find cream concealers to be the most malleable; they actually move with the skin tissue, which is especially good for the delicate area around the eye. Liquid concealers tend to be sheerer, while concealer sticks are usually thicker and heavier.

Concealer Placement in the Eye Area

- I suggest not placing concealer too close to the lash line. Many concealers contain oil and can cause mascara to bleed as the day goes on. (If you have trouble with bleeding mascara, try dusting a small amount of powder over the concealer to set it.)

- For dark circles, place concealer on the darker area under the eye, patting or brushing to blend. I find it best to layer lightly and build the coverage, rather than use one heavy application.

- For under-eye puffiness, do not place concealer (which is lighter than your skin tone) on the protruding area. Concealer placed on the "puff" will only accentuate it. Refer to the diagram below. The X's indicate where "not" to place concealer. Instead, place concealer on the darkest area which is indicated by the arrow. (Think of it as putting concealer "in the valley, not on the hill.")

PLACEMENT OF CONCEALER FOR UNDER-EYE PUFFINESS

There are different schools of thought as to whether concealer should be applied before or after foundation. I find that using concealer first works best, because if you use concealer after foundation and the concealer is too light, you may just find yourself looking like a wide-eyed raccoon. Foundation applied over concealer will blend in with your face tone.

In the order of makeup application, creams/liquids come before powders. (For example: foundation before powder, eyeliner before eye shadow, etc.) Powders set creams.

Foundation

As mentioned in the previous chapter, foundation is no longer used simply as a cover for imperfect skin. Today's formulations contain ingredients that are actually beneficial for protecting skin against damaging elements in the environment.

> The number one thing mature women do to age themselves is use too much foundation.

Types of Foundation

There are different types of foundations formulated for varying skin types, coverage, etc. Your lifestyle may be a factor in determining which foundation is best for you.

Tinted Moisturizers: Tinted moisturizers are designed to provide both moisture and minimal coverage. They combine two steps into one, thus saving time. They also usually contain sun protection.

Mineral Foundations: Mineral foundations come in both powder and liquid forms. The powder provides a matte/drier finish that should look like velvet, not dust. The minerals give a natural luminosity to the face.

I prefer pressed over loose mineral powder, because it has buildable coverage. My preference is also to apply pressed powder with a powder brush rather than a sponge or puff.

Cream Foundations: Cream foundation is considered the best choice for those with extremely dry skin. But beware of thick application—sheer is the key to a natural look.

Finding Your Perfect Match

Color is absolutely the most important element in foundation. A common question I am asked is, "How can I possibly find the correct shade of foundation when the lighting is so poor in department stores and you can't even sample makeup in those packages at drug stores?" Packaged products are the most difficult to try. But if you are sampling colors in a department store, try several shades on your jawline and take a mirror outside to look at your face in natural light to determine which is the best match.

Here are the steps I use to determine the correct foundation shade for a client:

1. Put 2–3 colors on your face at once. Blob them on and don't blend them into your skin. You really need to see what's on your face. It is easier to compare colors to see if they match the skin than to try on just one at a time.

2. Let them sit on your face for several minutes. Most women don't realize that foundation colors change within 20 minutes of the time of application. Mineral makeup has a tendency to darken as it warms up on the skin.

3. Ask yourself these questions:
    • Is the foundation lighter than my skin?
    • Darker?
    • Does it seem to disappear?
    • Does it appear too yellow, pink or gray?

4. If your face is a different shade than your neck, I usually match the foundation with the neck.

Ultimately, you want the color to disappear into your natural skin tone.

TIPS ON FOUNDATION

•   The best place to test a sample of foundation is on your jawline. But if you can't test the foundation there, place a sample on the inside of your forearm, because it is the closest to the color of your face.

- The more skin problems you have, the less foundation you should use.
- You may decide you like one type of foundation for work/dressier occasions and another for casual weekends.
- As the day wears on, foundation on oily skin tends to deepen, while foundation on drier skin tends to fade.
- Strive to use the least amount of foundation you can get away with. It will always look the most natural and youthful.

Powder

Years ago, women would apply makeup base over their entire face and neck then powder, powder, powder all over. Not anymore. These days, powder is used only for *staying power.*

For the most youthful look, use the least amount of foundation and powder you can get away with. Beware of chalky, heavy powders and those that tint your skin orange.

I have heard some say that you should not use powder if the weather is hot or muggy (or if you have a tendency to have hot flashes), but just the opposite is true. When it is humid and hot, I press, press, press the powder into the face then brush the excess off. (Sometimes if I'm doing the makeup for clients for a special occasion, I brush on so much powder they look as if they've just fallen into a flour barrel. But never fear, the powder evens out very quickly.) This is also a great tip if you have oily skin.

I love the ultra-light, whisper-bright translucent powder. I use it especially when I am applying makeup for a bride and she'll be in the spotlight for many hours. And because minerals and sunblock both reflect light, a dusting of powder in the t-zone helps control shine.

TIP: If you have an oozing blemish, you can dab a tiny dot of powder on the blemish to absorb the moisture, then pat concealer into the spot with a pointed brush for precise application.

Blush

The amount of blush we wear cycles with fashion seasons. It's always a good idea to scan the latest magazines to see what the current trend is, whether it be for blush, lip color, or eye color. I have never advocated being a slave to fashion, but keeping abreast of current trends introduces new options you can add to your personal makeup repertoire.

As a rule, cream blushes work best for drier skin and powder blushes for oily skin. Ultimately you want to find a formula that will last as long as you need it. Oftentimes, creams simply don't stay on as long. Layering is a great technique: apply cream blush followed by powder blush.

Because color in our face diminishes as we age, we can use blush to replenish that color and add a healthy, youthful glow. Is the blush you are wearing now giving you the appearance you want? Do you look energized, soft, lovely? It's a good idea to periodically compare the blush you are currently using to see if you need to adjust your color. Simply apply your blush to one side of the face and another shade to the other side. Can you see a difference? Don't just look at your cheeks, look at your entire face. What you are really after is a blush that helps your skin look fresher and more radiant.

I prefer applying blush with a dome-shaped brush that fits the cheek area (as opposed to a fat, fluffy brush for powder). If you must use one of those small, flat brushes that comes in the blush compact, follow the application by blending. Remember, the smaller/more dense the brush, the harsher the line. And bright blushes are harder to control, so it may be necessary to tone down the brightness by dusting a layer of powder over the color.

Proper placement of blush can give a lift to the face. Beginning no lower than the bottom of your nose, apply blush directly on the cheekbone, in an upward diagonal direction, to the hairline. (This is the most flattering

PLACEMENT OF BLUSH (UPWARD V)

and uplifting design for the mature face. It resembles the letter "V"—upward, just opposite of the pull of gravity.) Blushing the apples of the cheeks is fine for cherubic children, but may create jowls on a mature face when in repose.

EYES SEEK LIGHT AND COLOR

When you look at someone, whether you realize it or not, you are immediately drawn to the light and color in their face. You may have absolutely flawless skin, and be wearing no color on your face, but the woman next to you who doesn't have flawless skin but has on a complementary shade of lipstick will be noticed before you are. Why? Because our eye is immediately drawn to her color.

Lips

Lip Color

Lip color, again, is largely determined by the fashion season. Shiny, matte, or bold colors may be *en vogue* one day and pale, soft, or nude lips the next. Always choose colors, not because they are "on trend," but because they complement your skin and eyes. A lip color that has too much brown or gray in it can be very unflattering. And never choose a color that is duller than you are.

Here is my secret for finding the perfect shade of lip color: Stick the tip of your tongue between your teeth. Look at your tongue and choose a shade (in your clarity and brightness) that matches it exactly. What could look more natural?

Lipstick doesn't necessarily have to match your outfit. Once you find your perfect shades of pink, coral, and red, you can wear them with anything, and even combine them for a custom look. They will soon become part of your personal artist's palette. I've said it before and I will say it again: If the color goes with you and your skin, it will go with all your complementary outfits.

Not only do we lose color in our face as we mature, but our lips tend to fade as well. Lipstick shades that may have once been flattering can begin to look drab. The solution is simple—brighten up your face by brightening up your lip color.

FRESHEN YOUR COLOR
TO ENLIVEN YOUR LOOK

One client of mine had been using the same shade of lip color for years. When I asked her to empty her makeup bag, I found five lipsticks, all different brands, but practically all the same shade. I asked her to try on a lipstick within the same color family—the only difference was the color was about *two shades brighter* than what she had been wearing. (It was all about improving the clarity of the color.) What happened? Instantly, her eyes popped and her skin brightened. Nothing had changed except the color of her lipstick. Magic.

The real test came when she arrived home wearing the new lipstick. She asked her husband how he liked it. His response was, "It's a little bright, don't you think?" She immediately retreated to the bathroom, wiped off the new, put on her old color, then returned to her husband. His reaction: "Oh, heck, no. Go put on the new stuff—that color makes you look dead!"

TRUE STORY!

Now that you have determined your complementary shade, let's discuss application. I understand there are many long-lasting lipsticks in the market today. The idea behind these lip colors is that you won't have to reapply as often. But, they can be so drying. I'm sorry, ladies, the look is not pretty. I prefer a good lipstick with a lot of pigment. For more staying power, I advise simply:

- Apply lipstick precisely and rather heavily; blot.
- Apply again; blot.
- Apply again; blot. (Follow with lip gloss if desired.)

I like to use perm papers (ask your stylist or get them from the beauty supply store) to blot lipstick. It lifts the oil off, but not the pigment. This three-step process really stains the lip and you will be impressed with how well it wears.

Lip Liners

The purpose of lip liners is to define the shape of the lips (which may also mean disguising uneven lips) and to help keep lipstick from bleeding into the creases of the skin around your mouth. Using lip liners and lip colors that are the same or nearly the same color gives you the most natural look. Here are some tips on using lip liners:

- Outline and fill in your lips with a lip liner and follow with lipstick or a bit of gloss. This technique is long lasting, and when your lipstick wears off you are not left with a ring of liner around your mouth.

- For a romantic look, apply lipstick first, then finish with lip liner. This creates a softer line on the lips.

- Powdering the edge of skin next to the lips is a good way to retard lipstick bleeding.

- There are real differences in the quality of lip pencils. Automatic pencils tend to be softer.

- Lips tend to shrink as we mature. To create more fullness, or to balance a top lip with a fuller bottom lip, line from the outside corner inward to the cupid's bow. This creates more of an arch and gives the illusion of fuller lips.

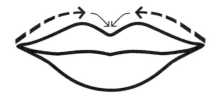

CREATING FULLNESS/BALANCE

Most mouths have two lip lines. One line delineates the shape and one delineates the color. It is often difficult to pinpoint your actual lip line. If you put powder on a cosmetic sponge and swipe it across the lips, the powder will collect on the ridge of the lips, defining them so the actual shape and edge are visible. (A tip to help smaller lips look fuller is to apply lipstick on the shaped ridge of the mouth, instead of just the colored portion.)

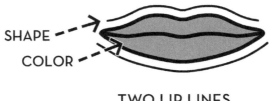

SHAPE

COLOR

TWO LIP LINES

ADDITIONAL
LIP TRICKS

- I advise my brides to use a lip stain as a primer before applying their lipstick. If you know you will be in the spotlight for many hours and can't reapply, when the lipstick eventually wears away, the stain will still be there. Test-drive this procedure *before* the big day.

- If your lipstick color seems too heavy or too deep, simply apply a bit of concealer over it to make it appear lighter.

- Since lips thin as we age, help them appear fuller by lining the outside with a white pencil, smudge, then fill in with lip color.

- When using lip gloss, be careful not to use so much that it causes the edges of your lipstick to bleed. Try dabbing a dot in the center of just your lower lip to add a bit of shine.

- Toothpaste is harsh and can dry lips. Before brushing your teeth, apply a layer of lip balm (preferably containing vitamin E) first. This will act as a conditioner. Then wipe lips before applying lip color.

"Before she allows the world to judge her face, a woman is entitled to create it."

—Kennedy Fraser

Eyes

Eyebrows

If you don't think your brows are vitally important to the entire look of your face, try this experiment: Draw in one brow with a brow pencil, and leave one as is. (Beware, if you are not used to seeing your brows done, it can be a bit frightening standing only inches away from the mirror.) Now, standing about five feet away from a full-length mirror, look at your face along with what you are wearing. Your made-up eye will absolutely look bigger than the unmade eye.

> ## INSTANT EYELIFT
> **Shaping and filling in brows gives an eye-popping lift to the face that no other technique can. Our eyes have a tendency to close down as we mature, so what better way to look more youthful than to give ourselves an eyelift!**

You can shape your brows using a powder and brush technique, but I prefer to use a pencil, because we have all grown up with pencils and I think they provide a bit more control. Here are tips I give my clients for attaining the most natural eyebrow look:

- When choosing an eyebrow color, look for one that most closely matches the roots of your hair.

- When shaping your brows, think of how a child might draw a roof on a house . . . pointing upward like an arrow. You will find this technique will lift your eye immediately.

- If you are a brow neophyte, start by using a brow pencil that is a lighter color than the roots of your hair. That way, you can put it on and if you feel it looks overdone, you can simply blend it in and it won't look so obvious.

- If you get out of line with your pencil, take a cotton swab and fine-tune the line where needed.

- Always look in a full-length mirror to help determine if your brows appear to be balanced with your outfit. Softer brows complement lighter colors, while darker colors need more brows.

- If you tend to be a bit of a "chicken" when it comes to applying brow pencil, it's a good idea to put your lip color on first. Then balance your brows with your lips.

Fashion trends tend to move toward either a soft eye/strong lip, or a strong eye/nude lip. You can experiment with these looks. A classic look is created when the eyes and lips are balanced.

Eye Primer

An eye primer, or "eye fix," is designed to help eye makeup stay on longer. It is applied on the lid to the brow. If you find that your eye shadow fades or creases during the course of the day, you may want to experiment with an eye primer. Eye primers are also great for those with thin-skinned eyelids, whose capillaries show through, creating a dark or pink appearance.

You may want to try different eye primer samples before you buy, since they are not all created equal.

Eyeliner

Eyeliner should be applied *before* eye shadow (powders set creams) for maximum staying power. Applying eyeliner first will also allow eye shadow to soften the look of a harsh line on your lid.

Color is important in everything, even eyeliner. Gentle coloring needs softer colors that do not create a hard line, such as dark gray or taupe, rather than black. Contrast color types usually like the impact of black, while Muted color types may want to use a deep brown. Experiment with different colors to find the one that's right for you.

Eyeliner is meant to define the eyes and makes them appear larger. But sometimes completely lining both the top and bottom closes up the eyes, instead of showcasing them. I see this technique used frequently by younger clients who tend to line both top and bottom lids with a harsh (usually black) eyeliner. The look may be dramatic, but can oftentimes look unflattering.

It's always good to ask yourself, "When people look at me, do they see my eyes or do they see my eye makeup?"

Eye Shadow

As a rule, neutral eye shadow colors seem to be the most timeless and classic, plus they are more natural and easier to wear. However, experimenting with different eye colors can be a fun, inexpensive way to add fashion flair.

Matching or not matching eye colors to your outfit is less significant than it once was. But this also cycles with style trends. Considering what looks best on *you* and goes with your personal style is most important. You can experiment and have fun with the color combinations, but don't be swayed by them. Play with them and ask yourself: "What is the look I am going for with the outfit I'm wearing?"

It is important to understand the fundamental concept that light colors "advance" and dark colors "recede." This principle can be used when applying makeup to areas you want to showcase or diminish. For example, if you have deep-set eyes, placing a light color in your crease and a darker shade on the ridge of the brow bone will give you a more wide-open appearance.

> The great thing about experimenting with eye shadow is that we have two eyes. Create two different looks and your mirror will tell you which one is the best.

Lash Primers

Lash primer is applied with a wand before mascara. It coats lashes so they appear fuller and longer. It is important to let the primer dry between coats and before applying mascara. Also, if the primer tends to clump lashes together, you can use an old mascara brush (that has been washed) to separate them.

Usually fewer applications of mascara are needed if you use a primer. (To see the difference lash primer makes, try it on one eye and not the other and compare.) Again, sample different primers as they are not all formulated alike.

Mascara

Mascara styles go in and out. Some seasons it may be a soft, natural lash look; other seasons it's bold, random, and messy. But there's one thing I know for sure: WOMEN LOVE THEIR LASHES.

Mascaras are formulated differently for different needs (for example, waterproof, sensitive, lash lengthening, thickening). Women with long, full lashes get the most results using a large brush with long bristles, while those with shorter, thinner lashes should use a small brush with short bristles. This is because the tiny bristles work well to pull, separate, and coat each individual lash.

Here is the proper way to apply mascara:

- Upper lashes: chin up, eyes down. Brush on mascara, lifting lashes to support curl.

- Allow your lashes to dry before you look up. If you drop your chin and look down to re-dip your wand, you may get spots of mascara on your lower brow area.

- Lower lashes: just the opposite. Chin down, eyes up.

- On humid days, allow mascara (and primer) more time to dry.

- If you don't like to wear eyeliner, really zigzag the mascara wand into the root of your lashes to get a more defined, thicker lash look.

CURLING YOUR LASHES

I cannot stress enough the importance of curling your lashes. Curling lashes is a wonderfully youthful thing to do. As we mature, our lashes bend downward (just like everything else). By lifting them and bringing them perpendicular to our viewer, we get a more wide-open, younger look.

Today you can buy the traditional hand-held lash curlers or even heated ones. (You can get the same effect heating a hand-held curler with your blow drier, because your lashes, like your hair, curl with heat. But watch out. The metal in the eyelash curler gets hot very quickly.)

I am often asked whether you should curl your lashes before or after a mascara application. In my opinion, it's better to curl lashes before applying primer or mascara, because if you use a squeeze curler and have already applied a coat of mascara, the lashes may stick to the curler and get pulled off your eyelid. Judge for yourself how long you should apply pressure with a lash curler. Long lashes may need two bends, one at the root and one in the middle of the lash.

You don't have to pull and stretch your face when applying mascara if you just hold it in the right position. And, for heaven's sake, don't dry your lashes with a blow drier as I have heard suggested. This can be very dangerous for the delicate tissue around the eye.

It is of utmost importance to know that mascara *must be replaced every 90 days*. Because the eyes are super-sensitive, manufacturers must formulate mascara using very mild preservatives. Since bacteria can grow in damp, dark places, a mascara tube is a perfect breeding ground for germs. And NEVER share your mascara. I tell my young clients if their friends ask to borrow their mascara, just give it to them. And don't take it back after someone else has used it.

EQUATING BEAUTY WITH BALANCE

Balance is a key principle to aesthetic design. Furthermore, studies have shown that facial symmetry is the most important element taken into consideration when determining facial attractiveness. Symmetry is at the core, along with youthfulness, smoothness of skin, and vivid color (e.g., in the eyes and hair). There seems to be universal agreement on this among people of different cultures, ethnicities, races, ages, and genders.

Years ago, a group of bridesmaids gathered in my studio while I was applying the bride's makeup. I overheard one young woman say, "Those magazine articles show you how to use makeup to disguise a long nose or a large forehead. But how do you know if you have a long nose or a large forehead?" Brilliant question.

The eye naturally perceives the face as ideal when it is divided into three equal portions:

- Hairline to brow
- Brow to tip of nose
- Tip of nose to bottom of chin

The face in the illustration below is divided into thirds.

DIVIDING THE FACE INTO THIRDS

Just as you can create the illusion of a slimmer, taller, or curvier body by styling your clothing, you can use makeup to design and style your face, so that features can be highlighted or disguised to appear more balanced. Simply remember the principle that *light* increases or maximizes, and *dark* recesses or minimizes.

Bronzer

Bronzers come in cream and powder form. A bronzer is actually intended to create shadow. Many women like to put it all over their face, so their face will match their tanned bodies. However, when you look at a photo of a model with really well-done makeup, her complexion is not all dark nor all light; it is the juxtaposition of the dark and the light together that adds drama and interest and enhances beauty.

Bronzer is not blush—it has a brown tint. (However, both blush and bronzer can be used for contouring.) To find the most compatible shade of bronzer, look for one that resembles a darker shade of your own skin.

Bronzer should be used anywhere you want to create a shadow, or want a feature to recede. It is most commonly used *under the cheekbones* to create a shadow, thereby helping cheekbones appear more prominent.

- If you have a wide face, brush bronzer around your jawline to make it appear less noticeable.

- Use bronzer on the forehead at the hairline if your forehead is the largest third of your face.

- For a long nose, place bronzer on the tip of the nose.

- If the longest third of your face is from nose to chin, brush bronzer on the tip of your chin.

Note: Many bronzers on the market are yellow based. If your skin is neutral, red, or pink based, be sure to select a harmonious color.

GLAMOUR TIP

If you really want to learn how to apply a makeup look you find in a magazine, try this trick: Turn the photograph upside down. You will be astonished at what you can see that you did not see before.

Look for nuances of layered shades of shadow, highlight accents on lips and cheekbones, or white liner on the inside corner of the eyes. Excellent makeup artists create this contrast between light and shadow. Looking upright and normal, the brain logically sees this darkness and lightness as natural. But upside down, your eye can precisely identify the color and product placement.

Highlighters

Just the opposite of a bronzer, which creates a shadow, is a highlighter, which creates iridescent light and draws your eye to that area. Highlighters should be finely milled and when placed on the face should look like candlelight rather than frost. Do not place highlighters in areas of your face where there are fine lines and creases. This will only bring attention to them.

Highlighting should be subtle and create nuance. Using a brush that is diffused helps keep the highlighter looking soft, without an obvious line.

In makeup design, it is important to remember *the eye seeks light and color.* This means you can apply highlighters and color on your face exactly where you want the focus to be. In effect, you can get people to look right where you want them to look.

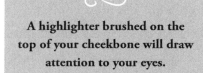

A highlighter brushed on the top of your cheekbone will draw attention to your eyes.

Brushes

People love to buy brushes in *sets.* I have never found this necessary. I believe you need the right brush for the right job. I mean, if I gave you a cotton swab to paint your house, it wouldn't be very practical would it?

The more compact the brush, the more definite the line; the larger and fluffier the brush, the less definite the line. The size of your face and scale of your features, along with the specific area of application, will literally determine the sizes of brushes you need.

Good-quality brushes will last a lifetime, but they do need to be taken care of. Brushes should be washed regularly. If you have dry skin, wash your brushes with shampoo. If you have oily skin, use dishwashing detergent. You will be amazed at how much powder, blush, and foundation residue is left in your sink when you clean them. Afterwards your brushes will look and feel as though they are brand new again. (Be sure to allow brushes to dry completely before using or storing.)

Hopefully, the information provided here will serve to simplify makeup matters for you. And although there may be differences in formulation, performance, and quality, makeup genius Wade Bandy summed it up best:

"It is the placement of the makeup, not the products that matter."

THE MANY MOODS OF MAKEUP

Just like swapping out pumps for sandals can completely transform the mood of an outfit, makeup can be changed to accommodate your different looks. A casual daytime event calls for softer, more natural-looking makeup that is not overdone, while a brighter, bolder look can add drama for an evening event.

And just as we can't assume one outfit will look the same as it does on our friend or someone we see in a magazine, the same holds true with makeup.

❧ 10 ❧

Personal &
Professional
POLISH

*"Image is information.
What are you broadcasting?"*

–Janna Beatty

As we near the end of this book, it is my sincere hope that you have begun to embrace an image of yourself that you would like to project to the world—an image that can only be defined by *you*, based on choices *you* make. The next step is to cultivate that image. It is interesting that, by definition, cultivate means "to promote or improve growth, by labor or attention." I believe it is this attention to detail that broadcasts our message.

Does your image match your inner spirit, or are you sending mixed messages? If people are sizing us up by our appearance, without us even uttering a word, then the language of clothing and grooming is hugely important.

Business Cultures

Whenever I present a talk to employees of a corporation, one of the main things I consider about my audience is the culture of their particular business. It is key when approaching the subject of dress and appearance. For example, traditional businesses such as banking, government, and law generally have a more tailored, conservative dress code, versus more creative, contemporary businesses where a dress code may not even be in existence.

Discussing what is suitable attire for the workplace is very difficult these days. For the most part, personal opinion, as well as company policies on dress code, determines appropriateness. However, at work the most important thing to understand is: *Your appearance is either an asset or a liability to your employer.*

What happens if you violate the dress code at the office? Obviously, it is insulting to be sent home, but guess what? It is also insulting to your supervisor or the HR person who must bring it up. It is not their job to *teach* you how to dress. They assume you already learned that at home. In my opinion, if someone shows up looking really spiffy for an interview and then turns up at the office dressed inappropriately, that is a breach of contract.

Employers don't care if you have a lot of outfits. The important thing is to look professional and appropriate. But whether the culture of your workplace is casual, trendy, or formal, there are certain grooming guidelines that apply in every situation.

Hair

Preferences in hairstyle and color are purely personal. Obviously, conservative and traditional business environments call for more polished, classic hairstyles.

If you are looking for a good/new stylist, I recommend you observe other people with similar hair types to your own. If you like a haircut, simply ask which stylist they use. If someone has just moved to a new city, I advise them to call the largest, most successful salon in town and ask for a stylist who is great at cutting their specific hair type (curly, thick, fine, etc.).

If you go to a new stylist, it may take a few visits for him/her to become familiar with the texture and growth pattern of your hair. Your individual hair type and hairstyle will determine how often to have it cut, colored, etc.

If you decide to color your hair, you really must make a commitment to it. Coloring takes time and effort, and can be costly, whether done at home or by a stylist. If you can see root growth, your hair won't look attractive or properly groomed.

Not only can hair color make you look and feel more attractive, but the chemical process may also improve your hair's texture, increase shine, and add body. Semi-permanent hair color is available so you can test colors before you make a commitment.

The texture of hair changes as it grays. I tell clients, "If your hair is gray, it should be shiny." Some women use a purple tinted shampoo on their gray hair to reduce yellowing and add a glossy brightness, but be aware that using too much, too often, can create a bluish tint to white hair. (Some older women, because of the hardening of their corneas, are unable to see the blue.) Of course, it is always important to check your hair color in natural light.

Nails

Once again, considering the context of the workplace, nails may run the gamut from conservative to high fashion. Generally speaking, the longer the fingernails, the less conservative. Though it cycles with popularity, a classic French manicure or clear polish is always appropriate. But no matter which style you prefer, be it trendy or natural, your nails should always be kept well-groomed.

Here are additional notes about nails:

- If you think of beauty as being equated with symmetry, it follows that the lengths of your nails should be kept uniform. It is best not to have several short nails while the rest are long.

- Square vs. round nails should be determined by what is most attractive to the particular shape of your fingers and hands.

- The more creative your workplace, the more creative you can be with your nails.

- It is extremely unprofessional to see chipped, partially painted nails. And a good rule is to keep nail polish remover in your desk at all times.

- Gel nails are extremely popular and offer great results, but upkeep does take a commitment of time and money. The upside is they can look fabulous for up to two weeks. It is a good idea to have the same color polish at home for nail touch-ups.

- If you want to try the newest nail fads, experiment on your toes. You can still have trendy nail art and wild colors, but it can be covered if necessary.

A senior client of mine (in her mid-80s) once told me that she had actually changed banking institutions because one of the bank employees she dealt with consistently had chipped nails with half-on/half-off polish. My client's nails were always meticulous. The point is, she got a negative impression of the bank employee and decided if the employee couldn't bother to take care of her own nails, how could she be trusted with a life's fortune?

Similarly, I recall the chief executive officer of a large company confiding in me that if he had to choose between two prospective employees with seemingly equal talents and resumes, the candidate with the shiniest shoes always got the job or promotion. The CEO equated competence with "attention to detail."

Nails, shoes, buttons. When it comes down to it, good grooming is all about attention to detail.

WHAT CAN MAKE YOU STAND OUT?

As an image consultant, I believe my job is to help people get more of whatever they want out of life by working with their appearance. Very often clients come to me with this question: "How can I compete with a sea of contenders for a job, a promotion, a date, or simply be memorable at a party?"

I say the easiest way to rise above the rest is to discover what is truly unique about you, and highlight that characteristic. If you have blue eyes, wear clothing that complements and enhances those eyes. Once I had a client whose last name was "Spot." When we put together different interviewing outfits, one piece of clothing always had polka dots incorporated into the pattern—whether it was in a blouse, a pocket square, or a scarf. Whatever it is, search it out and find it.

Of course, blue eyes and the surname "Spot" lent themselves to the aforementioned situations, but even if you don't have a characteristic quite this obvious, there is one thing *everyone* can do: get in the habit of being well-groomed. Grooming is that underlying element—that "something extra" people will remember about you. Each piece of clothing and every one of your movements has a message—a nonverbal language. Recognize this and you can outshine the others.

The ultimate answer is summed up this way: "If you want to be a standout, be *outstanding.*" Do your homework for an interview. Shine your shoes for a presentation. Press your clothing before a date. Send a hand-written thank you (not an email) promptly after an event. This attention to detail means you have gone that extra mile and your personal excellence will be remembered.

Each of us has a unique essence—tap into yours. When you do, you will gain the confidence to be yourself, as only you can be. Then you can go out and allow your brightest light to shine.

Casual Friday

To me, the topic of Casual Fridays has become totally hyped. To wear denim or not to wear denim, is that the question? If we are sending nonverbal messages and everybody is showing up looking like slackers on Fridays, what does it say about how seriously we take our jobs and ourselves?

I would rather redefine Casual Friday as "A Day to Easily Stand Out." Just imagine showing up at work on Friday looking a little more dapper, not out-of-place, but a tiny bit better-dressed than necessary. (You might say, polished casual with a bit of personality infusion.) This can really communicate a signal of confidence and credibility in the workplace.

Most importantly, Casual Friday shouldn't mean tattered or unkempt. Your attire should still look pressed and professional. The reality is that investing in your appearance is one way to help get those better managerial positions and bonuses. (Did you realize you could be perceived as a hard worker simply by looking more professional? Similarly, you may be seen as less productive simply by looking disheveled.)

Worth Mentioning

Fragrance

There is a zone surrounding you that includes the air others breathe, so it is absurd to think your preference for a delightful scent is going to be the same as everyone else's. Fragrance can be overpowering. I work right in people's faces, so I have to be conscious of fragrance, my breath, and even flowers in my studio.

Use fragrance sparingly, because it takes a while to warm up on the skin. And if you wear the same fragrance consistently, you can actually become so desensitized to it that you are no longer able to smell it.

Hint: Hold your perfume at arm's length, spritz one time into the air, and then step into it. That way, the concentration of the spray is more diffused when it hits your body.

NEVER: Spray perfume on neck or décolletage. If these areas are exposed to the sun, they are at risk for skin discoloration, because fragrance increases photosensitivity.

FRAGRANCE + SUN = BROWN SPOTS

Breath

There may be more to bad breath than just a heavy meal with garlic and onions. Dry mouth, gum infections, etc. may be contributors. If you have chronic bad breath, visit your dentist. He/she may simply advise you to use a tongue scraper or rinse with a more potent mouthwash.

Keep mints at your desk within easy reach. And if someone offers you a mint (whether for their sake or yours), it's usually a good idea to take it.

Body Odor

There is no excuse for body odor. Between deodorant soaps and clinical antiperspirants—no excuses, just clean yourself up.

Hosiery

In truth, I have seen teenagers who should wear hosiery and older women who look great with bare legs. The bottom line is, after you put on your outfit, look in the mirror wearing a stocking on one leg and no stocking on the other. Your eyes will tell you which works.

Grooming your gams is of the utmost importance, and there are great products to give your legs that sun-kissed look. Experiment with different brands to see which self-tanners work best for you. And as far as color goes, legs and arms should always look like they belong to the same body!

Clothing

Clothing should always be clean and pressed. Keep a small sewing kit in your desk for emergencies. It's also a good idea to keep a jacket (or appropriate third-layer piece) hanging on the back of your door, a clean shirt, and hosiery on hand, just in case.

If you are in doubt about the fit of a garment, take the **GAP TEST** in the dressing room before you buy it. *MOVE, SIT, BEND, and REACH* to simulate the movements you make at work. This will prevent surprise wardrobe malfunctions.

One basic garment I recommend all women have in their wardrobe is a skin-colored cami. A cami can convert any top to "workplace appropriate" by preventing cleavage from peeping through gaping button holes. (Tip: if you have a peep hole, use double stick tape on the problem area.)

Take into consideration that it's not just the clothing, but the body *in* the clothing that matters. Two girls may be wearing exactly the same dress but look totally different. If you have a slammin' body, choose clothing for the workplace that is not too fitted. And garments that are unlined or made from thin material may be better suited for evening.

What Is Inappropriate?

Overall, anything that is distracting to the job at hand can be considered inappropriate in the workplace: clothing that is too revealing, jangling jewelry, flip-flopping shoes, clacking heels, too much makeup or perfume, or not enough mouthwash or deodorant.

If in doubt, remember your manners. And manners can be summed up in three words: *respect for others.*

*"Respect for ourselves guides our morals;
respect for others guides our manners."*

–Laurence Sterne

Final
THOUGHTS

"You will find true success and happiness if you have only one goal . . . to fulfill the highest, most truthful expression of yourself as a human being."

–Oprah Winfrey

A friend of mine believes that a genius is anyone who has the ability to focus fully on something to get the desired results. And isn't it true that we can do *practically anything* if we make up our mind that it's a priority?

So what are *you* going to make your priority? How can you create more of what you want out of life? You must set your intentions and focus on achieving them, and follow-up by devising systems that support those intentions.

The only *constant* in our lives is *change*. Think about it. How has your life changed through the years? What different roles have you played so far? What roles are you playing now? What roles do you hope to play in the future?

John C. Maxwell declares, "Change is inevitable. Growth is optional." Are you fighting change at every turn, or are you accepting it, using it, and moving with it? When you embrace change you can confidently communicate who you are and support what you want and need. You can live your life based on present joy rather than past reminiscence.

"Change is the only promise life holds. Flow with life."

—Alexandra Stoddard

A smorgasbord of ideas has been presented here—ideas intended to help you define your own essence, cultivate your best looks, and communicate who you are through your signature style. This personal journey in self-discovery is meant to be fun and ultimately designed to help you gain the self-assurance to trust your own choices.

It is my hope that this book will move you to ask yourself, "Who am I today? And what do I want to accomplish tomorrow, and the next day, and the next?" You get to decide—you alone.

Only after you have defined your true essence can you share your quintessential self with the world, contributing what no other person on earth, from beginning to end, can contribute.

Enjoy your role in this magnificent life and never forget:

You are unique in all of time.

Acknowledgments

The evolution of this book could never have been possible without the revolutionary Color 1 Associates Color Analysis System devised by Joanne Nicholson and Judy Lewis-Crum. I owe them immeasurable gratitude for allowing me to work and study alongside them for the past 30 years.

To Jan Larkey, author of *Flatter Your Figure*. Thank you, Jan, for providing the most comprehensive informational guide on fixing figure flaws I have ever come across. My clients and I are grateful every day for the information you have imparted.

To my friend and colleague Colleen Moon, CEO of Complete Cosmetics Inc. and creator of Premiere Collection Skincare Products, the finest skincare line on the market. My clients continually thank me because their skin looks amazing, but it is your miraculous products that truly deserve the credit.

To Sarah Jo White. Thank you for taking our vision and creating a brilliant cover design that truly captures the essence of this book.

And to Jackie Barefield, our illustrator. Many thanks for sharing your amazing artistic talent. A picture is truly worth a thousand words.

We are enormously indebted to Becky White, Judy Cole, and authors Richard and Mary-Alice Jafolla for their editing assistance and guidance. Writing is rewriting, and our manuscript could not have become its finest without your help.

To Lillian Pearl Bridges, renowned authority on face reading. With gratitude for your belief and for convincing me that this manuscript must be created.

To my awesome assistants, Sherri Carrillo and Marsha Fitzjarrell, and also Diane Jordan. Thanks for holding down the fort so I could be available to write this book. I could never have done it without you.

To my talented and dear friend, Susie Hopson. Not only are you one of the top hair-stylists in the Southwest, but you are my personal style icon.

Sincere thanks to author JoAnn Jumper for her professional knowledge and personal support of our project. And to Lauren Wessinger, my friend and business counselor, and all the remarkable gals in my Ozsome Girls Group.

For their unwavering friendship and support, we thank Carla Stanley, Gayle Conger, and Lori Bruns. We appreciate you for never letting a day go by that you didn't ask about the book's progress, and encourage us at every crossroad.

To Wheatmark's Kat Gautreaux, Grael Norton, and Nicole Baron. Thanks to your professionalism, your attention to detail, and your unwavering support, our dream has come to full fruition.

To Ron and Joe—two amazing husbands. How did we get so lucky?
And to Blair, Keturi, and Airlie—true gifts.

Finally, we thank God, for a writing partnership and experience that was beyond perfect in every way. There are no words to express our gratitude . . . but You know.

References

Larkey, Jan. Flatter Your Figure. New York: Simon & Schuster, 1991.

Molloy, John T. Dress for Success. Warner Books, 1988.

Nicholson, Joanne & Lewis-Crum, Judy. Color Wonderful. New York: Bantam Books, 1986.

Rosetree, Rose. Founder of Face Reading Secrets®. www.rose-rosetree.com

www.Makeovers4u.com
www.QstyletheBook.com

ABOUT
THE
AUTHORS

Janna Beatty, owner of one of Texas' premier makeover studios, plunged into the study of image consultation when the field was still relatively new. After an education at the University of Southampton, England, Muskingum University, and the London Academy of Music and Dramatic Arts, and receiving a degree in Communications, several careers followed, including news anchor for one of television's top 100 stations. Then Janna discovered the image consulting business.

Janna has studied in New York and Paris with some of the most respected advisers in the fashion and beauty industry. Her knowledge of line, color, and makeup design is unparalled. The color system Janna has used her entire career is Color 1 Associates.

Janna insists, "After all that (study), it is the 30 years of working with my amazing clients that has taught me the most important thing—each person is unique, with his/her own beautiful possibilities." **www.makeovers4u.com**

Sharon White lives and writes in Temple, Texas. Her longstanding friendship with stylist Janna Beatty inspired her to co-write a book that would capture ideas Janna has been presenting to her clients for the past 30 years, in hopes of enlightening women about the infinite possibilities for enhancing their own "quintessential" style.

Catch our BLOG at www.qstylethebook.com

Photos by Doug Fitzjarrell,
Northern Horizons Photography

CPSIA information can be obtained at www.ICGtesting.com
Printed in the USA
LVOW01s0203091014

407851LV00001B/1/P